Including
Lower-
achievers
in the
Maths
Lesson

Diana Cobden
Sue Atkinson

HOPSCOTCH
EDUCATIONAL PUBLISHING

# Contents

Published by
Hopscotch Educational Publishing Ltd,
29 Waterloo Place,
Leamington Spa CV32 5LA
Tel: 01926 744227

© 2001 Hopscotch Educational Publishing

Written by Diana Cobden and Sue Atkinson
Series design by Blade Communications
Illustrated by Bernard Connors
Printed by Clintplan, Southam

ISBN 1-902239-57-1

Diana Cobden and Sue Atkinson hereby assert their moral right to be identified as the author of this work in accordance with the Copyright, Designs and Patents Act, 1988.

The author would like to thank the many teachers and children from the following schools who trialled these activities:

Upton House School, Windsor, Berkshire

Benyon Primary School, South Ockendon, Essex

St. Joseph's RC Primary School, Stanford le Hope, Essex

West Thurrock Primary School, Thurrock, Essex

Christ Church C of E Primary School, South Croydon

Haymerle Special School, London

Bishop Perrin School, Richmond

Sheen Mount Primary School, Richmond

Summerbee Junior School, Bournemouth, Dorset

St Ives First School, St Ives, Ringwood, Hampshire

Mudeford Junior School, Christchurch, Dorset

Linwood School (Special), Bournemouth, Dorset

In the section on Inclusion, The National Curriculum states that schools have a responsibility to provide a broad and balanced curriculum for all pupils. It sets out three principles that are essential to developing a more inclusive curriculum:

A: Setting suitable learning challenges

B: Responding to pupils' diverse learning needs

C: Overcoming potential barriers to learning and assessment…

*Including Lower-achievers in the Maths Lesson* is a series of books that gives support for including in the daily maths lesson those children in the class who, for whatever reason, are struggling and therefore often failing.

The books can be used alongside the **Developing Numeracy Skills** books also published by Hopscotch Educational Publishing Ltd. You will find a cross-reference to these books on the chart on page 5.

**CHAPTER CONTENT**

### The overall learning objectives

Each chapter has overall learning objectives that are based on the key objectives in the *National Numeracy Strategy Framework for Teaching*.

The grid on page 5 shows where these key objectives are covered within the chapters in this book. The lessons in this Year 3/P4 book are based on the Number Key Objectives for Years 1–4 (P2–5) to be found in the *Framework for Teaching*.

### The assessment focus

Each chapter is divided into 'sessions' – a set of activities that might last for one or more days. The assessment focus for each session is based on the key objectives and broken down into competencies that the children are expected to achieve within those key objectives.

An individual assessment chart can be found on pages 117 and 118.

### With the whole class

This section includes activities that are suitable for everyone in the class but they focus on the work for the lower-achievers that follows. Therefore they use easy numbers so that the lower-achievers can cope with the maths concept being taught.

You can repeat the whole-class starter(s) over several days or choose another starter that focuses on a similar learning objective.

Some suggested vocabulary is given, but you should teach with your *National Numeracy Strategy Mathematical Vocabulary* to hand.

### With  the lower-achievers

These are activities that follow on from the whole-class starter and you can use them:

● in the middle of the lesson for children who are under-achieving

● during the next week or two to consolidate the concepts

● when you come back to that topic next term.

Within this section is a selection of activities, some to be done with adult guidance and some which can be done by selected children independently.

*With adult support*

Many of the activities require equipment. We use equipment so that we are developing the children's mental images and things such as number lines, 100 squares and cubes are absolutely crucial. Many of the activities are games as these can motivate and keep the children involved. You will need to train your children to play games if they are not used to them.

Once taught, some of these activities can be teacher-independent. Often there are examples of questions and other things to say to the children so that their vocabulary is extended.

In addition to the adult support during the activities, try to plan for times when an adult can give a few minutes 'catch up' time to a group of children at odd moments during the day, for example five minutes at the end of assembly or at the start or end of the day. (If possible, take children from more than one class for 'catch up' times to make the best use of the time of an adult helper.)

*Teacher-independent activities*

These activities are suitable for lower-achievers to do on their own, depending how well they work independently.  Again, many of them will require the use of maths equipment.

### Plenary session

In this section a few questions are included to help lower-achievers reflect on their work, and sometimes there is an additional activity. Many of the whole-class starters can also be used as activities here.

Keep plenary sessions varied and interesting. They are times to sort out misconceptions, and times to generalise about what has been done. They are not just 'show and tell' times!

### The photocopiable resource sheets

Some of the activities suggested in the teachers' notes require the use of resource sheets. A minimum of words is used on these, so helpers will need to have instructions on what to ask the children to do on them. Many of the sheets are blanks, requiring the teacher or adult to write in tasks at a suitable level of ability.

On the more complex sheets for younger children there is a space at the bottom that contains notes for the adult. Sometimes this space is blank. This has been done deliberately as the teacher or adult may wish to add a few notes for another adult to use with a specific child or group. Likewise the sheets may be sent home to the parents/carers and this space can be used for instructions to them.

Some of the artwork on the resource sheets is on the same theme as the *Developing Numeracy Skills* books. However, some of it is more varied to provide interest for the children. We have also provided 'clip art' sheets at the end of the resource sheet section, so that you can cut and stick pictures onto the children's sheets in order to change the appearance of the sheets when you want to use them more than once. This gives the sheets new life and gives the children plenty of practice to consolidate.

### A general point about using the sheets with lower-achievers

Although the resource sheets provided in this book can be used several times, remember that it isn't recording maths that is important; it is whether the child can understand the concept. So use the sheets only when they are needed, such as for a teacher-independent activity or for assessment.

### Spinners

Some of the games in the book need a spinner that works by trapping a paper-clip in the middle of the spinner then flicking the paper-clip round with a finger. Spinners are quieter than dice and give more choice.

### Number lines

Have a large wall number line and 100 square up in each class. Remember that 100 squares are suitable for looking at patterns, such as for 10s, but are not ideal to do calculations on because children tend to get lost as they move from the end of one line to the start of the next. Number lines are much easier to use for calculations.

### And finally, remember

We want children to feel positive and to feel that they are achieving well in maths. Working endlessly on activity sheets can be boring, and could even make a child feel they are failing. Use games where possible to reinforce concepts and skills. Be generous with praise.

This grid is made up of the key objectives for Year 1/P2, Year 2/P3 and Year 3/P4 plus other crucial learning. It shows the chapter/s where these objectives are covered in this book. The grid also shows where the same area of learning can be found in the *Developing Numeracy Skills* series.

| KEY OBJECTIVES | CHAPTERS | DNS – BOOK/CHAPTER |
|---|---|---|
| Read, write and order whole numbers to at least 100 and know the value of each digit | 1, 2 | Year 3 – Chapters 1 – 3 |
| Use estimation for counting and ordering numbers | 1 | Year 3 – Chapters 1, 3, 6 |
| Compare and order numbers using a range of vocabulary and begin to use < and > | 2 | Year 3 – Chapters 2, 3 |
| Count collections of objects by grouping in 1's, 2's, 5's or 10's | 1, 2, 3 | Year 3 – Chapters 1, 2 |
| Counting on and back in 1's or 10's from a one- or two-digit number | 1, 2, 5 | Year 3 – Chapters 1, 3 |
| Give the number that is 1 or 10 more than a given number within numbers to 30 | 2, 5 | Year 3 – Chapter 3 |
| Recognise and extend simple number sequences (including odd/even numbers) | 1, 3, 4, 7 | Year 3 – Chapters 2, 3 |
| Recognise multiples of 2, 5 and 10 | 1, 7 | Year 3 – Chapters 2 |
| Recognise simple fractions such as $\frac{1}{2}$ and $\frac{1}{4}$ and use them to find fractions of shapes and numbers | 8 | Year 3 – Chapters 3, 10 |
| Understand that subtraction is the inverse of addition | 4, 5 | Year 3 – Chapters 4, 6 |
| Understand the operation of addition and subtraction (as take away or difference) and use the related vocabulary | 5, 6 | Year 3 – Chapters 4 – 6 |
| Make decisions about when to use addition or subtraction | 5 | Year 3 – Chapters 4, 5 |
| Know by heart all the addition and subtraction facts for each number to at least 10 | 5, 6 | Year 3 – Chapters 4 – 6 |
| Have a range of strategies for addition and subtraction | 4, 5, 6 | Year 3 – Chapters 4 – 6 |
| Use the strategy of doubling and halving | 4, 7 | Year 3 – Chapters 4, 5 |
| Understand multiplication as repeated addition | 3, 7 | Year 3 – Chapters 2, 7 |
| Describe arrays and know how this is linked to multiplication and division | 7 | Year 3 – Chapters 7 – 9 |
| Understand that division is the inverse of multiplication | 7 | Year 3 – Chapters 7 – 9 |
| Choose and use appropriate operations to solve word problems | 9 | Year 3 – Chapters 11 – 13 |
| Explain solutions to a range of problems using money, shape and measurement | 9 | Year 3 – Chapters 11 – 14 |
| Write number stories in response to a practical situation | 7, 9 | Year 3 – Chapters 11 – 14 |

# Counting and estimating

## Overall learning objectives

■ Be able to make sensible estimations and count with accuracy using different groupings.

■ Identify the position of numbers on a number line.

### Key words

| | |
|---|---|
| guess | about |
| estimate | approximately |
| nearly | tally |
| roughly | grouping |
| close to | |

# Count in groups

## Assessment focus

■ Can the children estimate the number of objects in a collection and count by grouping?

## Resources

■ large class number lines and 100 squares

■ Resource sheets 1, 2, 3, 4 and 5

■ collections of small items for grouping and counting, such as counters, cubes, money (2p, 5p and 10p coins), buttons, straws and elastic bands

■ some commercially-packed boxes of small things such as paper-clips or paper-fasteners

■ small plastic bags, jars and so on for collections

■ wrapping paper illustrated with lots of little pictures

■ sweets

## With the whole class

■ Seat the class in a large space, each child with a partner. Together count them in 2's. Ask someone to draw this as hops of 2 along the number line. Next, ask the children to sit in groups of 5 and count again. Again, write the hops on a number line. Finally, ask them to group themselves in 10's. Discuss when it is best to count in 1's, 2's, 5's or 10's.

■ Display a large number line. Show the class a jar containing a number of sweets. Ask around six children to estimate the number. Write their estimates on the number line. Ask *"Which is the highest/lowest estimate?"* and *"These children think there are between 38 and 51 sweets, so how can we check?"* When the children say *"By counting"*, give each group a collection of small objects in a bag or jar. One person in the group must estimate how many objects there are and mark it on a number line (Resource sheets 1, 2 or 3). They should then count the objects. When each group has finished counting, share the methods they used, stressing the value of counting in 2's, 5's or 10's.

■ Spend a few minutes counting in these groupings from 0–100, pointing to the numbers on the number line as they are said.

## With the lower-achievers

*With adult support*

**Choose from:**

1  Ask the children to hold up their hands to show 10 fingers. Count the fingers in 10's together around the group.

2  Display a 0–100 number line. Ask the children to help mark jumps of 10 starting at 0. Together count the multiples of 10, pointing to the numbers as you go. Ask questions such as *"When you start at 0 and count in 10's, what is the third number you say?"*, *"How many jumps of 10 are there between 0 and 100?"* and *"Which number will we land on if we count 5 children's fingers?"*

3  Using a collection of about 100 interlocking cubes, ask the children to estimate the number and write these estimates on a large sheet of paper. Discuss the estimates and the reasons why a number was chosen. Tell them to join the cubes in 10's and when they have finished count the 10's and then the extra ones. Show how they can make a tally of the 10's and 1's. Put out lots more cubes and ask each child to take about 50 by estimation and then by grouping in 10s and 1s count how near to 50 they were. Choose one child to say the number of cubes they counted and, using the number line, find how near to 50 the estimate was. *"Geeta had 58 cubes. Was that more or less than 50?*

*Let's count together how many more that was."* Let each child make a tally of their cubes and count in 5's.

4    Put on the table the boxes containing small things such as paper-clips or paper-fasteners which have the number printed on the box – the boxes do not need to be completely full. (These will usually be in 100's.) Talk about the quantity that should be in each box. Tell the children you want to check that there are the right number and ask how they will use grouping to count. If they don't suggest it, suggest grouping in 10's. Count these groups of 10 by counting 2, 4, 6, 8, 10. Then together count the groups in 10's to 100. Let the children work in pairs and when they have completed the grouping in 10's, ask them to say how many things were in their boxes. Did any boxes have the right number in and, if not, can the children count up on the number line to find how many more were needed to fill each box?

*Teacher-independent activities*

**Choose from:**

1    In pairs, the children could make a small poster of one of the following:

the number of fingers in the group – counting in 10's

the number of toes – counting in 10's

the number of eyes – counting in 2's

2    Give the group a small collection of 2p and 10p coins. Ask them to find out how many of each coin is in the collection and to use their number line (Resource sheets 1, 2 or 3) to count in 2's or 10's to find the value of each collection. Encourage them to find a way of recording their work. Extend this to counting in 5's using 5p pieces.

3    Use some plastic bags containing a number of straws, centicubes or buttons. Make sure there is not a mixture of different things in a bag. Ask the children to work in pairs first to estimate the number of objects in a bag, then to find how many there are by grouping in 10's with an elastic band, joining together or threading. Count up the bundles of 10's and then count on the extra bits.

4    Give the children some wrapping paper illustrated with lots of little pictures and ask them to count the pictures by grouping in 2's or 10's. Tallies can be made of the different groupings. Continue with grouping in 5's.

## Plenary session

■    *"How many hands with 10 fingers in your group? Shall we count them together?"*

■    *"Did you find it easier to count in 2's or 10's if you had lots of things to count?"*

■    *"Why was it useful to count in 2's to make your groups of 10, rather than 1's?"*

■    *"If you make a tally, what numbers do you count in?"* (5's)

■    Ask the children to explain to the class how they counted the contents of the boxes by grouping and to say how this helped. They can show their pattern of 10's and 1's on a number line, by hopping along the multiples of 10 and then the extra 1's.

# Where will it go?

## Assessment focus

■    Can the children estimate where numbers go on a number line?

## Resources

■    Resource sheets 6, 7, 8 and 9

■    a large class number line

■    tiles or number cards 0–100 and a bag

■    0–15 cards, cubes/counters

## With the whole class

■    Use a number 'washing line'. Put 0 at one end and 10 at the other:

|_____|_____|

0                                            10

Ask which number will go in the middle and why. Hold up a number less than 10 and ask someone to estimate its position along the line giving a reason for the decision. Do the others agree? Change the 10 to 20 and ask where that number goes now. What is the new middle number? Hold up other numbers for the children to estimate a position. *"Where will 13 go?"* and *"Why do you think it goes there?"* Alter 20 to another multiple of 10 and place the numbers. Work with a line that has numbers other than 0 and a multiple of 10 at the ends, such as the one below.

```
|_____|_____|
12            24
```

*"Where will you put 19?"*

Ask the children to show where in-between numbers might go.

■ Demonstrate how a number line can be used to help estimate the position of a number by highlighting a section, for example 10–18, and asking questions such as *"Which number is exactly between 10 and 18?"* Show how they can move forward in 1's from 10 and back from 18 until they find the middle. Pose other questions, such as *"Is 13 nearer to 6 or 18?"* or *"If you counted back 3 from 18 about where would you be on the line?"* Show how a number line can be used to help with the estimations.

## With the lower-achievers

### With adult support

**Choose from:**

1    Display a 0–100 number line with only the multiples of 10 marked. Working with the children, count the 10's together. Put a set of tiles numbered 0–100 into a bag and ask a child to take one out. Together talk about the number and which the significant digits are to help decide where to write it on the line. *"You have taken 37. Can you show us which of the 10's it goes between? Is it nearer 30 or 40?"* Let the children have several turns at choosing a

number, saying it and explaining where it goes on the line. Encourage the use of vocabulary for comparing numbers, for example 'more than', 'less than' and 'between'.

2    Give the children copies of Resource sheets 6 and/or 8 to complete. Give them assistance as necessary.

3    Ask two children to stand a short distance from each other. Say *"If Jake is 0 and Jess is 25, where will 15 be?"* Ask the group to help a child to stand where 15 would be.

### *Teacher-independent activities*

**Choose from:**

1    Give the children copies of Resource sheet 6. This gives follow-up practice at estimating the position of numbers on a number line. Remind the group that they can use a number line to help them decide where to put the numbers if they need one.

2    Give the children copies of Resource sheet 7 with just a start number and a finish number written in. Draw in some empty boxes and ask them to fill in all the missing numbers. See the example below.

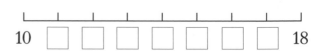

Remind the children that on a number line the numbers are spaced out evenly.

3   Introduce Resource sheet 8. Say that it uses a 0–30 number track and show the group how they can put a counter on their first number and count on from there.

The children need a set of 0–15 cards. They turn over two cards. One of the numbers is used as the start, the other as the 'count on' number. They have to count to find the number they land on.

4   Those children who need more counting practice can use Resource sheet 9 filled in like the one shown here.

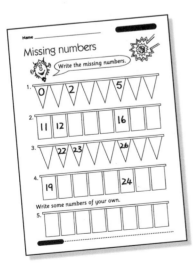

## Plenary session

- "Which two 10's numbers would you put 29 between?"

- "Which two numbers come after 56?"

- "Picture a number line. Put your finger on 6 and count on 5. Which number did you land on?"

- "Come and count on 4 starting at 5 on this number line."

- "What have you learned today about where to put numbers on the number line?"

- Repeat the activity with two children at the start and end of a number line, with other children positioning themselves at given places between them.

# Place value and ordering

## Overall learning objectives

■ Read, write and order whole numbers to at least 1000 and know what each digit represents.

> ### Key words
>
> | | |
> |---|---|
> | order | split |
> | next | tens |
> | before | hundreds |
> | greater than | units |
> | less than | compare |
> | represents | between |
> | partition | |

# All in order

## Assessment focus

■ Can the children put sets of numbers in order?

## Resources

■ number cards (large and small)

■ place value cards and number lines

■ counters

■ Resource sheets 1, 2, 3 and 10

■ arrow cards

## With the whole class

■ Ask three children to stand side by side at the front holding a large card between 0–9 each. Can the class say what number has been made? Write it on a piece of card. Ask the children to change places. What is the new number? Again, write it down. Let them make as many different

numbers as possible. (With three digits this should be six.) Ask which is the highest/lowest and which digit helps them to decide. Give the three-digit numbered cards to six children and ask them to fix them to the board in order. Repeat this with three new digits but, to help the lower-achievers, order the single digit numbers first, then make some two-digit numbers and order them, before going on to making and ordering three-digit numbers again.

## With the lower-achievers

### With adult support

**Choose from:**

1  Introduce the 'Target' game. Everyone needs a set of 0–9 cards placed face down on the table. Write a two-digit target number on the board. Ask the group to take two cards and make a two-digit number as near to the target number as possible. In turn, each child says their number and whether it is higher or lower than the target. Talk about the most significant number for deciding on size, for example looking at the 10's first and then the 1's. Ask *"Which number is nearest to the target?"* Together use a number line, highlight the target and mark each of the children's numbers on the line. The nearest scores 10 points, the next nearest gets 5.

2  Using place value cards, make some two-digit, then three-digit numbers, talking about the most significant digit. Check that the children understand why 519 is less than 591.

3  Give out copies of Resource sheet 10. Work with the group to put the one- and two-digit numbers in order from small to large and the other way round. It would be useful if they had a number line, such as on Resource sheet 1, to help them.

### Teacher-independent activities

**Choose from:**

1  Play 'All in order'. A pack of well shuffled 0–9 cards is needed for each player.

**Rules**

In pairs, the children put the cards in order from lowest to highest as quickly as possible. The player who orders the numbers first scores one point. Say that when they have repeated this several times they can then order the numbers in the reverse direction. The one scoring the highest number of points is the winner. Extend to numbers up to, and then beyond, 20.

2   Give out copies of Resource sheet 1, 2 or 3 which all contain number lines/tracks. Ask the children to practise putting sets of two-digit numbers in order from small to large and the other way round. They can extend this by making their own two-digit numbers with place value cards and ordering them.

3   Play 'Highest wins'. In groups of three or four, the children need two sets of 10's and 1's place value cards (100's could be added later) placed face down on the table.

**Rules**

In turn they take one of each card and make a two-digit number, saying the number they have made. Everyone writes all the numbers and, using a number line if necessary, they rewrite the numbers in order from highest to lowest. The person who made the highest number wins a counter. Cards are replaced and everyone has another turn. The player with the most counters wins.

## Plenary session

■   *"How do you know that 21 is a larger number than 13?"*

■   *"Which is the lower number, 71 or 17?"*

■   *"What did you learn today?"*

■   *"What did you enjoy most today?"*

■   Play 'Highest wins' with two teams.

# On and back

## Assessment focus

■   Can the children use a number line or 100 square to count on and back in 1's, 10's, and 100's?

## Resources

■   large and small number lines

■   a large 100 square and a large blank 100 square

■   Resource sheets 4, 11, 12 and 13

■   dice, counters, cubes, calculators and big pens

■   large numbers 1–100 (at least 20cm square cards, if possible)

## With the whole class

■   Sit the children in a large circle. Give two or three of the large number cards to each child. Say that they are going to make a really big number square on the floor. Say *"Who has got the number 1?"* Show them where the number square will start and the direction the rest of the cards will go in. The children with numbers 2–10 should place their cards and then those with 11–20. They could continue placing their numbers by taking turns around the circle so that they have to predict where their number might go.

■   Once the numbers are positioned, tell the children to close their eyes (and no peeping!) while you turn over some of the cards. Can they say which numbers have been turned over and explain why they think so? Ask someone to stand on a number, then go to the number that is 10 more, 1 more, 10 less or 1 less and so on, explaining their moves as they do so. Continue with standing on a number but counting on and back in multiples of 1 or 10.

# With the lower-achievers

## With adult support

### Choose from:

1   Show a 100 square with the numbers filled in and spend some time talking about the numbers that go under one another or by the side. Talk about adding or subtracting 1s and 10s depending on the direction to be moved from a starting number. Once the children have each had a few turns, hide the completed square and provide a large blank 100 square and big pens. Ask the children to help you write in the first row of numbers, 1–10 or 0–9. Continue by pointing to a space along the second row and asking a volunteer to say the number that goes there, then to write it. Do the others agree? Which numbers go on either side? Fill those in. Which number goes below – is it add or subtract 1 or 10? Continue in this way until all the numbers are filled in.

2   Cover up a number on the 100 square while the children close their eyes and ask them to say what it is. They must tell you how they know, talking about counting in 1's along the row, about 10 more and 10 less and about looking at the numbers above and below.

3   Give the children copies of Resource sheet 12 to complete. These are parts of a 100 square. Work closely with them.

## Teacher-independent activities

### Choose from:

1   Using Resource sheet 11, fill in the sheet, for example as shown here.

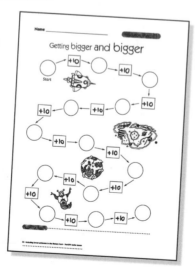

The children throw a dice for a start number and then keep adding 10 until the last space is filled. As this is a follow-up to the whole-class introduction the children might find a 100 square useful. (See also Chapter 5.)

2   Ask the group to complete the jigsaw pieces of a 100 square on Resource sheet 12. The pieces have only one or two of the numbers filled in and the children need to write the missing ones. Encourage them to think about the missing numbers but make 100 squares available for support if needed.

3   Give the children copies of Resource sheet 4 and tell them to cut along some of the lines to make jigsaw pieces for their friends. Each piece will need to have about 10 numbers in it. Children who are struggling could cut just along straight lines (rows or columns). The children swap puzzle pieces and put each other's squares back together.

4   Play the game 'On and back in 10's and 1's' using Resource sheet 13 filled in, for example as below.

The children need a copy of the sheet between two of them, counters in two colours and a +1, +1, −1, +10, +10, −10 dice. Make a calculator and/or a 100 square available to help with checking answers.

### Rules

The children take turns to throw the dice, choose one of the numbers on the sheet, add or subtract the number on the dice and say the answer. Their partner should check their answer with a calculator or 100 square. If they are right, the player puts one of their colour counters on the number. They should take turns like this, the winner making a row of three counters.

## Plenary session

- ■ *"Which number comes before 15? Is that add or subtract 1 or 10?"*

- ■ *"Is 42 ten more or ten less than 32?"*

- ■ *"What is our maths about this week? How do you think it will help you to learn these things?"*

- ■ Draw up some parts of a 100 square on the board as on Resource sheet 12 and ask the children to fill in the numbers, explaining how they know the missing numbers.

- ■ Do plenty of adding in 10's in mental maths time over the next few weeks as it is a fundamental skill for mental calculations.

# Into 10's

## Assessment focus

- ■ Can the children group into 10's and 1's for counting and use partitioning?

## Resources

- ■ dice and cubes
- ■ place value cards
- ■ 1p, 10p and £1 coins
- ■ number tiles or cards and a bag
- ■ Resource sheets 14 and 15

## With the whole class

- ■ Put a large number of interlocking cubes on each table and give the children place value cards. (Give the higher achievers more than 100 cubes.) Tell the children to count their cubes as quickly as possible by grouping them into 10's and 1's. (To encourage quick counting, remind

the children to count in 2's to make up each 10.) When they have finished ask someone from each group to write their number on the board. Discuss how many tens and units there are in each of the numbers and how they might be made with place value cards. Write several two-digit numbers on the board. Point to one and ask the children to make it as quickly as possible with place value cards. Repeat this with all the numbers before extending to three-digit numbers.

## With the lower-achievers

*With adult support*

**Choose from:**

1  Give the group some 1p, 10p and £1 coins. Ask how many pence equal 10p and how many 10p coins make £1. Tell them to make 19p using 1p and 10p coins, then add another 2p. Count the number of 1p coins again and ask *"Have you got enough to change 1p coins into a 10p?"* When the exchange has been made talk about the total amount of money (21p). Do a few more examples carrying out the exchanges together by counting in 10's.

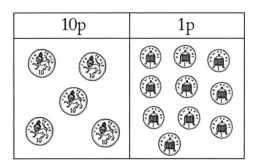

Say that they are now going to play a game with a partner to see who can be the first to get 50p. In turn they throw a dice and take that many pennies. When all the spaces for 1p are covered the pennies are exchanged for 10p.

2  Play 'First to £1' with the whole group. Cover the table with a large sheet of paper and put a collection of 1p and 10p coins out.

**Rules**

Each player throws a 0–9 dice (or spinner), in turn, and takes the number of pence equal to the dice score. The score is written on a part of the paper nearest the player. After the first round discuss who has most/least pence. Play continues and the player can either keep a running total or write the second amount to be added later. Ask *"Can anyone make 10p in 1p's yet?"* If they can, the player changes the ten 1p coins for a 10p. As the game progresses, ask questions about who has the most 10p coins and how much this is altogether. The winner is the first person to collect £1. The game can be played in reverse with players starting with £1.

### Teacher-independent activities

**Choose from:**

1   Using Resource sheet 14, the children can play a place value game. Pairs of children need interlocking cubes, a 1, 1, 2, 2, 3, 3 dice and a game board each. In turns, the players throw the dice and take that number of cubes which they place on the dog outline. One dog picture is covered at a time. The winner is the first player to cover all three dogs. The number of complete dogs is counted and so are the separate parts. Players then count the total number of their cubes and make their number with place value cards to show at the plenary session.

2   Using Resource sheet 15, ask the children to choose how many lots of 10 stamps to cut out, and how many 1's. They count up their groups of 10 and the extra ones, stick the stamps in their books or on a piece of paper and write the two-digit number.

3   Give the children some cards with two-digit numbers written on them and some interlocking cubes. Say that you want them to take a card, count out that number of cubes and put them together in 10's and 1's. For example, using the number card 36, a child makes 3 'wands' of 10 and 6 more. They next use a 30 and 6 place value card to show 36. The children should draw what they did to share in the plenary session.

4   Pairs of children need a bag containing tiles with two-digit numbers written on them and some 10's and 1's place value cards. They take a number from the bag and make it with the

place value cards, writing both the first number and the partitioned number, for example 36 and 30 + 6.

## Plenary session

■   Make some more two-digit numbers with place value cards.

■   *"How many lots of 10 in 53?"*

■   *"Which number is made up of 6 tens and 1 unit?"*

■   *"Which number can be partitioned into 30 and 4?"*

■   *"If you have 45p, how many 10p coins could you have?"*

■   *"When you have 10 one penny coins, what can you exchange them for?"*

■   *"If I had an enormous pile of sweets, how could I find out how many?"* (Make sure the lower-achievers know that to find how many there are, grouping in 10's can help.)

# Bigger and smaller

## Resources

■   0–20 cards

■   a bag and number tiles or cards

■   0–50 number lines, such as Resource sheet 3

■   Resource sheet 16

■   numbers 0–30 (or more) written on star shapes and a bag

■   a dice

## Assessment focus

■   Can the children compare and order numbers using a range of vocabulary, such as larger/smaller and more than/less than, and begin to use the symbols?

## With the whole class

■   Play 'I'm thinking of a number'. Say *"I am thinking of a number and you have to find out what it is by asking 'more than' or 'less than' questions. I will only answer 'yes' or 'no'."* Give an example, *"Is it more than 20?"* so that the children get the idea that they can narrow down the options in this way. Once they are confident let them spend a few minutes playing in small groups of three to four. Continue by asking them to use 0–20 cards to show the answers to questions involving comparative words. For example, *"Show me a number that is 2 more than 8,"* or *"Show me a number 10 smaller than 22."*

■ Draw four boxes on the board with a > (greater than) symbol between each pair of boxes, such as below.

Invite four children to the front. Ask them each to take a card from a 0–9 pack which is placed face down. They each write their number on the board. The numbers might be 6, 3, 7 and 1. Now ask them to decide which boxes the numbers could go in to make the sentence correct, having first reminded the class that they are using the 'greater than' symbol. Discuss the different ways the four numbers could be arranged in the boxes to make the sentence true. Repeat this with four more numbers but using the < (less than) symbol. Show the children needing more support how they can use a number line to compare numbers because the nearer to the right the higher the number. Extend this to three-digit numbers.

## With the lower-achievers

### With adult support

**Choose from:**

1   Play 'Lucky dip'. Each pair of children has a bag of number tiles, some of which are duplicated. Ask one pair to start. Each child takes a number from the bag and writes it on the board. Compare the two numbers. Ask which is the lower number. The person with the lower number wins a point. If the numbers are the same both players score a point. Show them how to record the numbers using the < symbol, for example 14 < 22.

2   Display a 0–100 number line to help the children with comparing numbers. Ask which end has the higher/lower numbers. Point to two numbers and ask which is higher and which is lower and show how this can be recorded using the > and < symbols. Tell all the children to take four cards from a 0–9 set and make 2 two-digit numbers. Ask them to say the numbers and which is higher/lower. Can they explain how they know? Let them record in two ways, such as 21 < 34, 34 > 21. Using the same four cards the group rearranges them to make new two-digit numbers and repeats the comparisons. As the children work, talk to them about ways for deciding highest/lowers numbers. At the end of the session ask questions such as, *"Did anyone make a number higher than 90? How many more was that?"* and *"What was the lowest number you each made? Was Toby's lower or higher than Suzie's?"*

3   Play 'As high as the stars'. You need the numbers 0–100 (fewer numbers can be used, possibly 0–30) written on star shapes, and a number line.

**Rules**

Pick a star out of the bag. Show the children the number. Each child then picks a star out of the bag. If their star number is higher than yours they can keep it, but the lower numbered stars must be put back. The number line can be referred to for checking the higher/lower numbers. The winner is the player with the most stars.

*Teacher-independent activities*

**Choose from:**

1   Playing in pairs, the children need two sets of 0–20 cards that have been well shuffled and placed face down on the table. In turn, both players turn over the top card from each set. The player with the higher number keeps both cards. Continue until all the cards have been taken. The player with the most cards wins. Repeat this game but this time the lower number wins.

2   Let the children each work with two sets of 0–5 cards, Resource sheet 3 (a 0–50 number line)

and Resource sheet 16. Remind them they will be doing the same thing as they did in the whole-class session and to remember to make 2 two-digit numbers. The larger number should be written in the first box and the smaller one in the second, then vice versa.

3    Repeat the activity above but this time the children turn over two cards and write the two-digit number in the first boxes. They then turn over two more cards and make a two-digit number to write in the second box. If the statement is true they draw a tick, or a cross if it is wrong.

## Plenary session

■   *"How do you know that 12 is less than 22?"*

■   *"Can you show how to write 16 is greater than 8?"*

■   *"Is this a true statement, 15 is less than 4?"*

■   Play a game similar to that in the starter session with the four boxes and the greater than symbol, but this time throw a dice and the children have to decide which box to place the number in. Once a number is placed it cannot be moved. Try to make the statement in the four boxes true.

■   Ask some of the group to explain the game of 'As high as the stars' and the methods they used for deciding which numbers were higher.

■   *"What have you learned while we've been doing this work about ordering numbers and place value?"*

# Number sequences

## Overall learning objectives

- Describe and extend simple number sequences (including odd and even numbers), count on or back in 1's or 10's from a given number.

> ### Key words
>
> | | |
> |---|---|
> | predict | odd |
> | continue | even |
> | sequence | pair |
> | next | multiple of 2 |
> | before | every |
> | pattern | every other |
> | rule | |

# Making pairs

## Assessment focus

- Can the children recognise and use odd and even numbers?

## Resources

- cubes, play people, sorting toys and so on
- number lines and number cards
- large pens and sheets of paper
- hoops or circles drawn on large sheets of paper and labelled
- a pack of cards and a dice
- Resource sheets 17, 18 and 19

## With the whole class

- Display a large 0–100 number line and give each child 20 cubes. Ask them to pick up several cubes, count how many there are and try to put them into pairs. Ask them to tell you which numbers between 1 and 20 make pairs. Explain that this is the same as dividing by 2. Circle these numbers on the number line. Can the children find all the numbers divisible by 2? Explain that these are even numbers. Then in pairs ask them to find all the even numbers between 20 and 40. Again circle them on the number line. Count them together, continuing until 100 is reached.

- Explain that the numbers that cannot be divided by 2 are called odd numbers. Ask them to make some odd numbers with their cubes and circle these in a different colour on the number line before counting all the odd numbers up to 100.

- Give a start and an end number. Ask the class to count between these in 2's, with a child pointing to the numbers. For example, *"Start at 4 and end at 18."* Pose questions such as *"Give me an odd number between 58 and 62."* Give the lower-achievers pairs of numbers you know they can work with.

## With the lower-achievers

*With adult support*

**Choose from:**

1   Ask the children to model a set of numbers from 1 to 10 using interlocking cubes, one colour for each number. For example, 3 has 3 red cubes and 4 has 4 green cubes. Ask which are odd and which are even numbers, asking *"How do you know that number is odd/even?"* Record the odd and even numbers on a large sheet of paper. Tell the group to link the models of 1 and 2, thus adding them together. *"How many is that? Is the answer odd or even?"* Continue with linking 2 and 3, then 3 and 4, asking the same questions. Can the children circle the answers on the number line? Ask *"Are the pairs of numbers you added odd or even?"*, *"What if we added 10 and 11?"*, *"How could we get an even answer?"*, *"What do you notice about the numbers that make pairs?"* and *"Which is the smallest/largest even number you have found?"*

2   Give the children copies of Resource sheet 17. Tell them that the robot likes to eat even numbers but spits out the others. They should take a handful of cubes and try to put them into pairs. If they make pairs they then count the cubes and write the number on the robot's 'tummy'. If the number is odd it is written in the dustbin. Observe – who is still not clear about odds and evens? With these children, look at the endings, for example 1, 3, 5, 7 and 9.

*Teacher-independent activities*

**Choose from:**

1   Prepare a large sheet of paper with two circles drawn on it labelled 'odd numbers' and 'even numbers'. Using play people or cubes, tell the children to take a handful each and try to put them into pairs. If a pair can be made they count the number of play people and write it in the even numbers circle. If a pair cannot be made the number is written in the odd numbers circle.

2   Using Resource sheet 18, the children throw two dice and write the numbers in the first two squares. They add the two numbers and decide if the result is odd or even, by counting and pairing cubes if necessary. They then circle 'odd' or 'even' according to the result. The activity can be extended by using a 1–9 dice.

3   The children can play 'Even number snap' using a pack of cards with the picture cards removed. Pairs of even numbers can be 'snapped'.

4   Give the children Resource sheet 19. For question 3, they first fill in the consecutive numbers on the triangle. Then odd numbers are coloured blue and the evens are coloured red. Discuss the patterns made by the odds and evens.

## Plenary session

- Ask those children who completed Resource sheet 17 what they noticed about the units in odd or even numbers.

- Ask those children who completed Resource sheet 19 to predict how the pattern might continue if another row of triangles is drawn. Ask *"What would happen if we wrote numbers on squared paper and coloured odds and evens?"*

- *"Find 14 on your number line. Do you think it is odd or even? Why is that?"*

- *"How do you know that number is even?"*

- *"What do you know about the units digits in even numbers?"*

# What does it end in?

## Assessment focus

- Can the children recognise two-digit multiples of 2, 5 and 10?

## Resources

- large and individual 0–100 number lines and 0–9 cards

- cubes and pens

- 0–99 square made using Resource sheet 5

- Resource sheets 1 and 2

## With the whole class

- Display the large 0–100 number line. Ask several children to stand at the front. Tell them you are going to count their eyes. Begin by counting in 1's, but then say you will count in 2's. Show that one pair is 2 eyes, two pairs equal 4 and so on. Ask one of the children to circle the numbers on the number line, making reference to the number pattern.

- Practise counting on and back in 2's. Give the children some numbers and ask *"If we count in 2's will we reach this number? Explain how you know."* Ask another group to face the class, each holding up one hand. Count the fingers on one hand, then two hands and so on. Circle the numbers on the number line with a different colour and practise counting in 5's. Ask *"Will we reach 47 if we count in 5's? How do you know?"* and *"What do all the numbers we have used end in?"* Continue with the children holding up both hands and counting in 10's. Mark these on the number line.

- Show the children how to use the constant function on a calculator, using an OHP calculator if possible. $1 + = = =$ will produce the counting numbers, although on some calculators the $+$ sign might need to be pressed twice. Write the sequence of key presses on the board to help this group and let them spend some time experimenting.

Tell the group that once they have managed to make the calculator count numbers they are going to make it 'count' in 2's in the same way, except that 2 is pressed instead of 1. Encourage them to record the pattern of 2's on a 100 square. They should continue in the same way, finding the pattern of 10's and then of 5's. During the plenary session they can look at their 100 squares and tell the class which numbers are multiples of 2, 5 and 10.

## With the lower-achievers

*With adult support*

**Choose from:**

1   Together, circle all the even numbers on a 0–99 square (or a smaller square, depending on the group's experiences), discussing the pattern made. Say the repeating pattern of 0, 2, 4, 6, 8 together. Using two cards from the 0–9 set challenge them to make a number ending in one of those numbers and say what it is. Do this several times.

2   Give out a collection of numbers written on cards. Ask the children to sort out the multiples of 2 into a sorting circle. Ask *"Why did you put that number in the circle?"* Continue with the multiples of 5 and 10.

*Teacher-independent activities*

**Choose from:**

1   Using 0–30 number lines (Resource sheet 2) the children should work together in pairs to circle the multiples of 2 in red, and then write each number on a separate card. They do the same with the multiples of 5 (in green) and 10 (in blue). The numbers are placed face down on the table in a rectangular array. One at a time the children turn over two cards. If the two numbers are both multiples of 2, or 5 or 10 that person keeps the cards, otherwise they are replaced. The person with the largest number of pairs is the winner.

2   Using a 0–50 or 0–100 number line/track (Resource sheet 1 if appropriate), explain to the children that they will be using the line/track to

count on in 10's using different starting numbers. Using a set of 0–9 cards they turn over a card to give the start number, which they write down. Then they keep counting on 10 more and recording the sequence, until they reach the highest possible number on the line. Once they are confident, they can start from a two-digit number, recording on an empty number line.

## Plenary session

■   *"If you count in 10's from 0, what digit will be at the end of each number?"*

■   *"How did you know that is a number in the 5 times table?"*

■   *"You made the pattern, 2, 12, 22, 32, 42 and so on using a number line. Can you show me that pattern on the 100 square?"*

■   *"Tell us how to make a calculator count in 2's."*

■   *"Who would like more help with recognising multiples of 2, 5 and 10?"*

# What is missing?

## Assessment focus

■   Can the children complete a given number sequence and describe the rule?

## Resources

■   a function machine box

■   a range of number lines including a Unifix or Centicube line

■   Resource sheets 9, 20, 21, 59 and 60

■   number cards, cubes and counters

## With the whole class

■   Talk about machines the children will be familiar with, such as a washing machine. It has an input in the form of the washing going in, a function of the clothes being washed and an output of clean clothes. Say that today they will be thinking about this type of machine except that numbers will be going into and out of the 'machine'. Use a shoe box with holes at either end that will hold a sliding tray and a hole in the top where objects can be added.

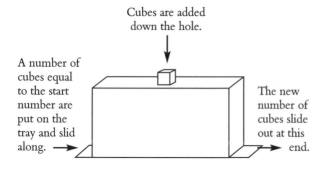

Cubes are added down the hole.

A number of cubes equal to the start number are put on the tray and slid along.

The new number of cubes slide out at this end.

Stick a +1 label on the front and explain that if 2 cubes go in, 1 will be added. Ask *"So what comes out?"* Demonstrate how it works. *"What will come out next time if the answer is put back in?"* Keep repeating this and show on the board how the input and output can be recorded. (See Resource sheet 21.)

## With the lower-achievers

### *With adult support*

**Choose from:**

1   Use a large sheet of squared paper (4cm squared, if possible). Write the numbers 1–6 along the top and down the side as shown below and fill in some of the numbers to get the children started.

| + | 1 | 2 | 3 | 4 | 5 | 6 |
|---|---|---|---|---|---|---|
| 1 | 2 | 3 | 4 | 5 | 6 | 7 |
| 2 | 3 | 4 | 5 | 6 | 7 | 8 |
| 3 | 4 | 5 | 6 | 7 | 8 | 9 |
| 4 | 5 | 6 | 7 | 8 | 9 | 10 |
| 5 | 6 | 7 | 8 | 9 | 10 | 11 |
| 6 | 7 | 8 | 9 | 10 | 11 | 12 |

Show the group how to continue by making a 6 x 6 addition square, letting them use cubes or counters, if necessary. Together look for number patterns. For example, *"Can you find the diagonal even number patterns?"* Ask for predictions, such as *"What number would come after 2, 4, 6, 8, 10, 12 in the diagonal pattern?"* Circle all the even numbers and discuss the patterns. What can they say about the numbers that are not circled?

2   Play 'What's my rule?'

**Rules**

Using number cards, start off some sequences and ask the group *"What comes next?"* Some examples of sequences are on Resource sheet 20 and you can focus on multiples of 2, 5 and 10. Observe – who needs more help counting forwards and backwards in 2's, 5's and 10's? Can the children tell you the rule for each sequence?

### *Teacher-independent activities*

**Choose from:**

1   Let the children use a 'function machine' box, in pairs, to explore number patterns, starting with adding 1 to each consecutive number from 1–5 (or beyond) and recording this on Resource sheet 21. During the plenary session ask the group to share their observations.

2   Give the children number lines with two numbers the same distance apart as an interlocking cube (see below) or use plastic number lines that fit with cubes. The children should find number patterns and facts using the lines and cubes. For example, the diagram below shows a number line with 3 cubes, so the children can find add or subtract patterns for the numeral 3 (3, 6, 9 and so on).

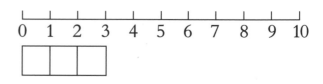

Encourage them to work systematically. They should record by circling the numbers on a number line, or with different colours of cubes, for example 3 red, 3 blue and 3 green.

3   Let the children use a number line to help
    them complete Resource sheet 20. Encourage
    prediction of the next numbers in each series.
    They can use Resource sheet 9 for further
    practice, using a different picture from Resource
    sheets 59 or 60.

## Plenary session

■ *"How do you know that will be the next number?"*

■ *"What is the rule for this sequence?"*

■ *"What would the pattern be if you counted back in 2's
   from 19?"*

■ Let the children work in pairs to make up a
   number sequence for others to continue and say
   the rule.

■ *"What was our lesson about today? What did you
   learn?"*

■ Play 'What's my rule?' in two teams, scoring 2
   for each correct answer.

■ Give further practice in counting backwards in
   number sequences.

# Strategies for addition

## Overall learning objectives

■ Use knowledge that addition can be done in any order to do mental calculations more efficiently.

> ### Key words
>
> | | |
> |---|---|
> | method | plus |
> | explain | altogether |
> | tens boundary | total |
> | make tens | different way |
> | in any order | work out |
> | add | solve |

# Try it different ways

## Assessment focus

■ Can the children add three or more numbers and explain how they worked?

## Resources

■ number cards, tiles or counters numbered 0–5 in small bags and another collection numbered 0–20

■ dominoes and dice

■ cubes

■ number lines and 100 squares

■ Resource sheets 22, 23, 24, 25 and 26

■ large 0–30 number cards

## With the whole class

■ Display a large 0–100 number line. From a set of large 0–30 cards ask one of the children to pick out two of them. Ask another child to find these numbers on the number line. Can anyone say which is the smaller and which the larger of the two numbers and explain how they know?

■ Tell the children you now want them to add the two numbers together. Write the calculation on the board. Ask some children to explain what they did to get the answer. Various strategies may have been used, such as using doubles or near doubles. Say that now they are going to work on adding two numbers by putting the larger number first. Repeat the activity several more times, asking different children to write the sum on the board. (To make sure they work with a large number and a small number, you could put the cards 25–30 in one pile and 3–9 in another. Ensure that they pick up one from the pile of large numbers and one from the pile of small numbers.) Once they are confident, extend this to three numbers, writing them in order of size before adding them. (But be aware that children will use a range of strategies for mental addition.)

## With the lower-achievers

*With adult support*

**Choose from:**

1 Display a 0–30 number line. Ask three children to throw a 0–9 dice in turn and to write their number on a large sheet of paper. Say that together they are going to add the three numbers. Talk about which of the three numbers is the highest/lowest and which might be the best way of adding them. Together add the numbers by counting on along the number line. Ask one of the children to write the numbers in a different order and add them again. Use the dice to get three more numbers and ask the children to add them together using a different order each time. Encourage them to put the numbers in order first. *"Can you write these three numbers in order with the largest first?"*

2 Show the children how to play the 'Aim for 10' game on Resource sheet 22. Using a 'dartboard', the children have to add three of the numbers to make the target in the centre. Numbers can be used more than once.

3 Using two piles of numbers, as in the whole-class starter session (one pile 3–9 and another 25–30), let the children pick up from the 3–9 pile first, then physically change around the two numbers. Ask *"Why do we change 3 + 29 to 29 + 3?"*

*Teacher-independent activities*

**Choose from:**

1   Play 'Highest wins'. Each pair of children needs a small bag containing several tiles or cards numbered 0–5 or above. The children play in pairs, taking turns to take three tiles. Each player should write their numbers in order. Using apparatus or a number line, the three numbers are added and the player with the highest answer wins a point. During the plenary session ask the children to explain their methods, for example did they put the larger number first? Did this make it easier?

2   Play 'Aim for 10' using Resource sheet 22. Using a 'dartboard', the children have to add three of the numbers to make the target in the centre. Tell them that numbers can be used more than once. The target can be made higher or lower using Resource sheet 23 depending on the group's experiences.

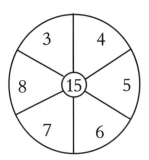

3   Play 'Making towers'. The children take 10 interlocking cubes and find ways of arranging them into three towers. Encourage them to record what they have done, either in drawings or numbers.

4   On Resource sheet 24, six numbers are given and the children have to find which three total the number on the balloon label, then write them on the balloons. In the lower part of the page they choose six more numbers and make up their own sums.

5   Use Resource sheet 25 to give the children experience adding four numbers. Answers can be found by counting spots but encourage them to check by adding the same numbers on a number line. A simpler activity is to use only

one domino and record by drawing the spots. Additional practice can be given by using Resource sheet 26.

## Plenary session

- "If we add the numbers in a different order will we get the same or a different answer?"

- "Is it easier to put the larger or the smaller number first? Why is that?"

- Give the children repeated practice at explaining how they do calculations, gradually developing their vocabulary.

# Spotting the 10's

## Assessment focus

Can the children add numbers by finding pairs that make 10?

## Resources

- dice, cubes and counters
- 1p, 2p and 5p coins
- 0–10 cards
- small items that are priced or Resource sheet 60
- Resource sheets 27, 28, 29, 30 and 31
- a number line

## With the whole class

- Write lots of single digit numbers randomly on the board.

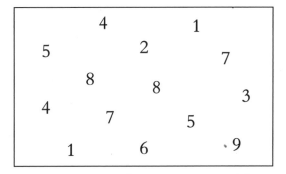

Tell the children they are going to be '10 spotters' and to look at and think about the numbers. Ask if anyone can spot a way of making 10 and come and show it on the board. This can be done by circling a pair or several numbers and joining them with a line, or by writing them as a sum.

■ Play 'Ping pong' to 10. You say a number between zero and 10 and the children must reply with the number that makes it up to 10. So if you say 6, the children reply 4. To keep them on their toes, occasionally say "Ping" and the children have to reply "Pong". You need to play this game repeatedly until all the children can give quick responses. You could write the number bonds to 10 on the board to help with later parts of these lessons.

■ Write a collection of about five or six numbers lower than 10, making sure there are some pairs that add to 10. Ask the class to add by spotting 10s. Explain that this is a useful strategy for adding several numbers together.

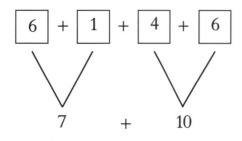

## With the lower-achievers

### With adult support

**Choose from:**

1   Draw a large version of the board of one of the boards on Resource sheet 30. Point to a number and ask the children to make a 'wand' with the same number of cubes. Can they take the right number of cubes to make a total of 10 and use them to make two of the other numbers on the board? For example, if you point to 6 the children will need 4 more cubes. They can be split to make either 2 and 2 or 3 and 1. Work practically until the children are confident and then let them use Resource sheet 30.

2   Give the children a collection of small items that are priced so that pairs adding to 10p can be found. Alternatively, use the money clip art on Resource sheet 60, cut out and enlarged and completed with plenty of prices that will make 10p, such as 6p and 4p. Ask them to choose three things each trying to make sure that the prices of two of them total 10p, then find the total cost. Then give them copies of Resource sheet 28. You need to fill in the box to buy either two or three things.

3   Take several sets of 0–10 cards, shuffle them and deal them out. The children have to race to put them in pairs to make 10, for example 6 and 4, 9 and 1 and so on. Play this several times, keeping the score.

### Teacher-independent activities

**Choose from:**

1   Use Resource sheet 27 as a follow-up to the whole-class session. Remind the children to look at the number bonds on the board to help them. They can also choose some equipment to help them.

2   Play the 'Race game' using Resource sheet 31 filled in like this.

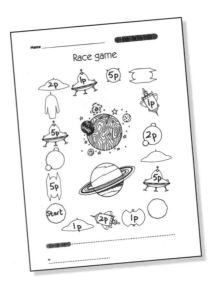

You need a 1–6 dice, 1p, 2p and 5p coins and a counter for each player. Players take turns to throw the dice and move that many spaces, in any direction. If they land on a 1p, 2p or 5p, they take a coin of that value from the bank. The aim is to be the first to total 20 pence.

3   The children will need a collection of small items that are priced so that pairs adding to 10p can be found. Ask them to choose three things each trying to make sure that the prices of two of them total 10p, then find the total cost. They can use copies of Resource sheet 28 to record their findings.

4   Play the 'The adding game' on Resource sheet 29. Before they start, remind the children to think about ways of making 10. Each player needs a sheet. They take turns to throw three dice, adding the numbers together using the number line and writing the number on one of the aliens on their sheet. When all the aliens have a number on them, they can throw the dice again but this time cross out the totals as they are made. The first player to cross out all their numbers wins.

## Plenary session

- ■ *"I am pointing to 4. How many more do you need to make 10?"*

- ■ *"Can you think of two numbers that add up to 6?"*

- ■ *"Is there another way you could split up 6?"*

- ■ *"Why do you think we are learning to find ways to make 10?"*

- ■ Play 'Ping pong' to 10 again. Repeat this game over the next few weeks and play to 20 as well.

# Number bonds and patterns

## Assessment focus

- ■ Can the children recognise and use patterns in addition, particularly to make the number bonds of 10 and 20?

## Resources

- ■ a large 100 square and number line
- ■ 1p, 2p, 5p and 10p coins
- ■ counters and cubes
- ■ Resource sheets 9, 31, 32, 33, 34 and 59

## With the whole class

- ■ Make up a story about two aliens, one a happy alien who can change her number and the other a sad alien whose number always stays the same. Choose a starting number, such as 1, and say that this time the happy alien will add 10 to her number each time. The sad alien can only have 2 each time. Continue with the pattern, asking someone to point it out on a 100 square. Let the children predict the pattern.

| | | | | |
|---|---|---|---|---|
| 1 | + | 2 | = | 3 |
| 11 | + | 2 | = | 13 |
| 21 | + | 2 | = | 23 |

- ■ Give further examples, such as 'add 5 each time'. Change the position of the aliens so the sad one is first and starts. Then continue another number pattern and talk about it. When the children are confident start with 2 two-digit numbers, for example 12 + 14, and make a +10 sequence:

$$22 + 14 = 36$$

$$32 + 14 = 46...$$

# With the lower-achievers

## With adult support

### Choose from:

1   Start by showing the group a large 100 square and together say the multiples of 10 as you point to them with an alien's special pointer. Point to a one-digit number. Can the children say the number? Can anyone point to the number that is 10 more? Say the sequence together. Repeat this several times, writing the sequences on the board, for example:

  $3 + 10 = 13$

  $13 + 10 = 23$

  $23 + 10 = 33 \ldots$

  Discuss the number patterns. You could record answers on Resource sheet 9, changing the picture to one from Resource sheet 59.

2   Provide some 10p, 5p, 2p and 1p coins. Ask the children to take a 10p coin and add 1p. How much does this total? How much will they have if they add 10p and another 10p and so on? In pairs, let them take an amount under 10p, then keep adding 10p coins. They should keep a record of the amounts they have, using a number line if necessary.

## Teacher-independent activities

### Choose from:

1   Let the children play 'The race game' on Resource sheet 31. Fill in each spaceship with any numbers up to 20. The children use one copy of the sheet between two players.

### Rules

i   They choose a starting point and move in opposite directions around the board. In turn they look at the number they are on (such as 15) and say how many must be added or subtracted to make the number on the next spaceship. If the target number is 20 and they are on 15 they must say *"Add 5"*.

ii  Their partner checks and if the answer is wrong they stay on that number. If the answer is correct they move on one space and wait for their next turn.

iii The winner is the first to get all the way round.

2   Using Resource sheet 32, the children have to join up pairs of numbers that total 10 and then write the number bonds to 10 in order. Extend the activity to number bonds to 20, starting with $10 + 10$, $11 + 9$ and so on. Let the children record these any way they want. Draw their attention to the patterns.

3   Using Resource sheet 33, set the children tasks to find patterns. For example, if the first block is a set of calculations all with add 10, put +10 at the top and suggest starting numbers to suit your children, such as 1–6 adding 10 each time.

4   Using Resource sheet 34, the children can play the 'Three in a row' game.

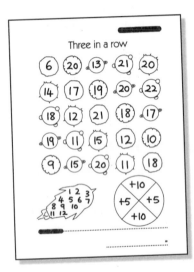

This example uses +5 and +10, but you could add any number you want. Ask the children about the pattern that they can see when they add 10 to a number.

### Rules

i   To play, you need two players, cubes in two colours and one sheet between the two players.

ii  Players take turns to choose a number from the rocket and another from the circle. They add them together and cover the number they make with one of their colour counters.

iii The first to make three in a row is the winner.

iv  To make a longer game that depends a bit more on luck (so the lower-achievers have more chance of winning), use the circle as a spinner rather than just choosing any number you want.

## Plenary session

- *"Can you tell me something you notice about the pattern?"*

- *"How much will you have if you start with 6p, add 10p and another 10p?"*

- *"How could you go on with this pattern? 12 add 10, 12 add 20, 12 add 30."*

- *"If 18 add 10 is 28, what is 19 add 10?"*

- *"Did you enjoy making patterns? What did you learn?"*

- *"What have you enjoyed most in maths this term?"*

- *"When you played 'Three in a row' did you get good at seeing the add 10 pattern?"*

- Play a 'Three in a row' game in pairs, enlarging Resource sheet 34 and using Blu-tack to hold up the counters.

# Linking addition and subtraction

## Overall learning objectives

■ Understand that subtraction is the inverse of addition and state the subtraction facts corresponding to a given addition and vice versa.

> ### Key words
>
> inverse          altogether
> opposite         total
> subtraction undoes   take away
> addition         equals
> add              tens boundary
> plus

# Add or subtract?

## Assessment focus

■ Can the children make decisions about addition and subtraction?

## Resources

■ interlocking cubes, counters and so on

■ number lines and a 100 square

■ large and small 1–20 cards and '+', '–' and '=' cards

■ Resource sheets 35, 36, 37 and 38 (You need to use Resource sheet 36 to make several sets of cards.)

## With the whole class

■ Ask two children to stand side by side at the front and give each a number card between 1 and 20. Ask the others what calculation they need to do to change one into the other. For example, the two children have 3 and 8, so 5 must be added to 3 to make 8. Ask other children to hold cards to show the sum:

| 5 | + | 3 | = | 8 |

What happens if the children change places and 8 has to change to 3?

| 8 | ? | ? | = | 3 |

Make sure the children know what the '+' and '–' cards mean.

■ Write about eight numbers between 1 and 20 in a circle on the board.

(circle of numbers, clockwise from top: 10, 14, 7, 1, 16, 5, 7, 1; with "+4" between 10 and 14, and "-7" between 14 and 7)

Point to one of the numbers, for example 10, and say *"If you go round the circle in a clockwise direction, what do you have to do to make 14? Do you have to add or subtract?"* Write the calculations between each pair of numbers. Discuss how to decide on the calculation needed and expect them to say that if the first number is smaller than the second they add and vice versa. Do the children expect to get the same answers if they go the opposite way round? Can they explain their reasoning?

## With the lower-achievers

*With adult support*

**Choose from:**

1  Plan some addition and subtraction stories to discuss and work through with the group, with the aim of helping them make decisions about the type of calculation needed. These might relate to the theme of space. For example, *"When it got dark, 3 spaceships appeared. 2 more joined them. How many spaceships were in the sky?"*

and *"An alien had 10 pet creatures. He sold 5, so how many were left?"* After discussing some examples, write up two numbers and together make up a story that uses them, using the appropriate operation card. Then ask the group to work in pairs to make up a word problem for the others to do. Talk about the key words that might help us to decide whether to add or subtract. Follow this up by using Resource sheet 37. Talk about how you could make up a different story with the same picture. Question 1 on Resource sheet 37 could be 5 aliens and 2 running away and this would be 5 − 2 = 3.

2   Show how loop cards work using Resource sheets 35 or 36 cut up into cards. Suggest the children choose a card to start with, do the calculation and find a card with the answer. (You can start anywhere in the loop.) So the card with 12 and +5 leads to the card with 17 and −7. They continue until all the cards make a 'loop' with all the calculations leading to answers. Let the children decide on a method of recording. (The principle of making your own loop cards on sheet 36 is that the last card and the first card must link. So on sheet 35, the last card is 6 +6 making the 12 of the first card.)

***Teacher-independent activities***

**Choose from:**

1   Give a set of loop cards to each pair of children. When they have made their loop they can swap their set for another one.

2   Use Resource sheet 38 filled in like this.

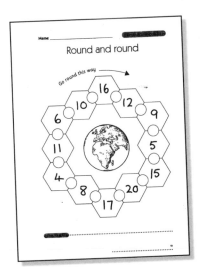

The children can start anywhere and they fill in the circles with the calculation that they need to get from one hexagon to the next. Suggest that they use a number line to help them decide on the calculation that they need. Remind them that if they count back they are subtracting and if counting on they are adding. Use Resource sheet 38 to make other examples, such as adding and subtracting 10 or 9.

3   Using 0–9 cards, the children turn over four of them and put them in a line. They have to work out the calculation to move from one number card to the next.

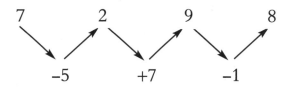

Let them record in their own way.

## Plenary session

- Prepare a large copy of Resource sheet 38 and play with one team going around one way and the other team going around the other way. What happens to the calculations in the circles? (If they add 4 going one way, that becomes subtract 4 going the other way.)

- *"What is the answer if you have to get from 3 to 6? What if you have to get from 6 to 3? How are they different?"*

- *"What do you have to do to get the answer to this question: A family of 3 children and 2 adults goes on a spaceship ride. How many people altogether?"*

- *"Tell us a number story, Lisa, where you have to take away. Which operation card do you need?"*

- *"If I tell you a story with 'and 3 more came along'/ 'altogether makes'/'leave' in it, would it be adding or subtracting?"*

# Know one fact and three more

## Assessment focus

- Can the children use corresponding addition and subtraction facts?

## Resources

- cubes
- butter-beans painted on one side (nail varnish or felt-tipped pens works well) or counters with a coloured spot on one side
- plastic cups
- Blu-tack
- sentence maker
- a number line, number cards, blank cards and '+', '–' and '=' cards
- Resource sheets 39 and 40

## With the whole class

- Provide the children with interlocking cubes in three colours. Use big number cards and '+', '–' and '=' cards. Blu-tack three numbers to the board, for example 4, 8 and 12 and ask the children to model the numbers with cubes using a different colour for each. Invite a volunteer to use the numbers and signs to make a number sentence, for example 4 + 8 = 12. Talk about how the three colours of cubes show this. Ask what other number sentences they can write using these three numbers. Talk about how these are related numbers because you can use them to make more than one calculation.

## With the lower-achievers

*With adult support*

**Choose from:**

1   Let the children work with number and '+', '–' and '=' cards on a sentence maker or boards and Blu-tack. Write up another three related numbers, for example 5, 7 and 12. Say a number sentence in words and ask the children to make the sentence, then model it with cubes. Ask them to make a new sentence using the same three numbers, and tell the rest of the group what has been done in words and then to write up the sentence for everyone to share. Encourage them to write all the possible sentences with the numbers, using addition and subtraction to show at the plenary session. Use a range of vocabulary, such as plus, minus, add, subtract and equals.

2   Use a large 0–20 number line or make one by writing the numbers on scrap paper and placing them on the floor. Ask a child to stand on 10 then take 3 steps forward and land on 13. Ask *"What happens if you now take 3 steps back?"* (You get back to where you started.) This can be recorded using Resource sheet 39. (See the example on page 30.)

3   Ask the children to choose three numbers that could make number sentences. Observe – who has grasped that the numbers need to relate to each other?

*Teacher-independent activities*

**Choose from:**

1   Play 'Spill the beans'. Make up a story about an alien who has found a clever way to find number sentences using addition and subtraction. Each person needs some butter-beans that are painted on one side and a plastic cup. The children take a small handful of beans, count them and then put them into the cup. The number can be written on the outside. The beans are tipped out. Some show their white side and others the colour. The three numbers are used to make four addition and subtraction facts. Encourage recording of the number facts, in pictures if necessary.

This shows:

$4 + 5 = 9$

$5 + 4 = 9$

$9 - 5 = 4$

$9 - 4 = 5$

2   Resource sheet 39 encourages the children to understand that subtraction is the inverse of addition. Fill in the sheet as shown below, leaving blanks for the children to complete.

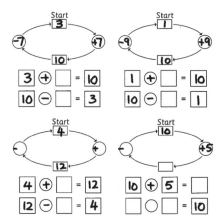

3   Give the children some sets of three numbers to work with and ask them to write the four related addition and subtraction sentences. They can use Resource sheet 40 to record this.

## Plenary session

■   *"Dani and Shazi, show us the sentences you made. How do you know when you have three related numbers? Would this activity work with 10, 3 and 4?"* (No)

■   *"Darren, tell us three related numbers."*

■   *"Did anyone learn a new word today? Tell us a sentence with 'difference between' in it."*

■   *"Can you write 15 subtract 5 on the board? What other facts do you know that use the same numbers?"*

■   *"If 5 plus 6 equals 11, what does 11 minus 5 equal?"*

# On and back in 1's and 10's

## Assessment focus

■   Can the children add or subtract multiples of 1 or 10 from a given number?

## Resources

■   colouring pencils

■   dice

■   a large 100 square and number cards

■   Resource sheets 1, 2, 3, 4, 34 and 41

## With the whole class

■   Display a large 100 square. Point to a low number and ask what 10 more is, what 20 more is and so on. Go to a higher number and ask what 10 less is.

■   After a while ask the children to shut their eyes and picture the 100 square in their minds. Ask them mentally to put a counter on a number, such as 15, and then write down the numbers above, below and at either side, which in this case are 5, 25, 14 and 16.

■   Ask for the answers to 15 – 10, 15 + 10, 15 – 1 and 15 + 1 and ask how this is the same as their mental picture of the 100 square. Put the class into two teams without the 100 square on display. Ask pairs to visualise a number then add or subtract multiples of 1 or 10. The fastest to call out the answer each time scores a point for their team.

## With the lower-achievers

### *With adult support*

### Choose from:

1   Display a large version of Resource sheet 41 and give the children a 100 square. Write a single-digit number in the top left circle. Show the arrow pointing to the right and ask what

number will go in the next circle. Continue moving to the right and filling in numbers with the group. Next fill in the other numbers by adding 10 to numbers going down the page and 1 to those going right. Ask questions such as, *"So, if 13 add 10 is 23, what is 13 add 20?"* Let the children have their own starting number and record what they do on Resource sheet 41.

2  Let the children take turns to take a 0–9 card, then count on in 10's up to or beyond 100. Observe – who needs more help with this? Those who are confident can move on to a different activity. Work with those who need help by doing 'add 10' patterns on a 100 square.

3  Play 'Three in a row' in two teams, using an enlarged copy of Resource sheet 34. Write numbers such as 14, 24, 17 and 38 on the rocket. In the circle put 'add 10', 'add 20' and 'add 30'. Cover the planets that contain the answers with a counter. For example, 14 + 30 is 44. The teams can take turns to choose a planet to cover with a colour counter, trying to make three counters in a row. Observe – who is securely adding multiples of 10?

### *Teacher-independent activities*

### Choose from:

1  Play the 'Very long sum' game. Each child needs a 100 square, or number line (Resource sheets 1–4), colouring pencils and a 1, 1, 1, 10, 10, 10 dice. Working in pairs, players start at 0, throw the dice and add the number thrown with the aim of reaching 100. Encourage them to record on their 100 square, circling their number in a colour, and with a calculation, such as

$$0 + 10 = 10$$
$$10 + \ 1 = 11$$
$$11 + 10 = 21$$

The winner is the first to reach exactly 100, for which they score 100. If they pass 100, they score 50. They can play again using a different colouring pencil. The game can be altered so they work back to 0 by subtracting either 1 or 10 depending on the dice throws.

2  Give the children a number line to suit their experience, such as on Resource sheets 2 and 3.

Ask them to find a start number by turning over a 0–9 card and to keep adding on in 10's along the number line, recording all the numbers as they land on them. Repeat this using a different colour pencil and a different 'start' number.

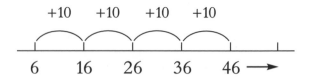

## Plenary session

■  *"On the 100 square can you point to 25? What is 25 + 10? What is 25 + 30? How did you work it out?"*

■  *"Find 99 on the 100 square. What is 99 take away 20?"*

■  Give lots of experience at mental maths time for the next few weeks in adding and subtracting 10 so that all the children can do it quickly and explain the pattern. Encourage them to verbalise that when you add multiples of 10, the units digit stays the same, but when you add 1's, the units digit changes but the 10's digit stays the same.

■  Play 'Three in a row' in two teams again, this time adding 40, 50 and 60 each time.

# Using number lines

## Overall learning objectives

- Use known facts, including place value, for addition and subtraction and partition numbers into tens and units.

> ### Key words
>
> | steps on the | add |
> | number line | subtraction |
> | count on/back | minus |
> | addition | tens boundary |
> | plus | difference |

# Hopping on and back

## Assessment focus

- Can the children use a number line for addition and subtraction?

## Resources

- 0–9 cards and place value cards
- dice
- number lines and 100 squares
- Resource sheets 3, 4, 42, 43 and 44

## With the whole class

- Draw a long 0–100 number line on the board with only multiples of 10 marked. Give some quick examples for the children to answer with addition and subtraction, such as *"50 subtract 30".*

- Continue by asking what they might do for 10 + 16. Some of them might reply that it is the same as 10 + 10 + 6. Give several similar examples to help the lower-achievers to split the numbers into 10's and 1's, starting each time from a multiple of 10. Extend the activity to start on numbers that are not multiples of 10.

To do 26 + 17 = 43:

first do 26 + 10 = 36

then 36 + 4 = 40 and

40 + 3 = 43; so 26 + 17 = 43.

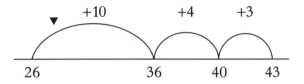

- Give two more numbers and show how the same method can be used for subtraction, using either counting back or counting on.

## With the lower-achievers

*With adult support*

**Choose from:**

1 Write on the board a two-digit number greater than 20. Talk about which part represents the 10's and which the units and ask the children to make the number with place value cards. Can they explain how many 10's there are in the number? So if the number was 28, can they talk about it as 10 + 10 + 8? Give them some other numbers they can partition in this way.

2 Draw an empty number line on a board and write a single-digit number at the start, such as 3. Say that they are now going to add 23 to that number by splitting the 23 into 10's and 1's:

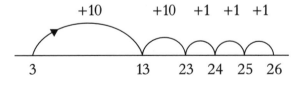

Do several examples together and then give the group some numbers to add or subtract using this strategy.

*Teacher-independent activities*

**Choose from:**

1  The children need Resource sheet 42 cut into squares. (When the numbers are matched correctly they add to 100. You can use Resource sheet 43 to make similar games to other totals.) Using a number line, the children work with a partner to list all the pairs of numbers making 100, using multiples of 5 (5 + 95, 10 + 90, 15 + 85 and so on). They use this information to help them match the pairs of numbers on the puzzle.

2  With their 0–9 cards, challenge the children to make a two-digit number. Starting with this number, they then throw a 1–9 dice and another marked +, +, +, –, –, – and add or subtract the number shown on the dice by counting along the number line and recording, for example 45 + 4 = 49.

3  Using place value cards 10–30 and 0–9 cards, the children can make a pair of two-digit numbers or you can give them some cards with one- or two-digit numbers to work with. Using Resource sheet 2 or 3 with the numbers written in, they ring the two numbers and then draw two hops between them to show two numbers that can be added to the start number to reach the second one:

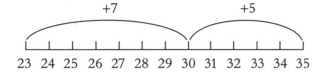

4  Resource sheet 44 gives the children partitioned numbers to add to multiples of 10 as a continuation of the whole-class introduction. Let them use 0–50 number lines (Resource sheet 3) with all the numbers marked to help with counting on and back. This gives experience in adding pairs of two-digit numbers without crossing a 10's boundary.

## Plenary session

■ Ask some children to come and draw some hops along a number line, checking that they are partitioning numbers appropriately.

■ *"Picture a number line in your head. Your finger is on 13. How many do you count back to reach 10?"*

■ *"Think of a number line. You start at 20 and count on 6. Where do you land?"*

■ *"What did you like best in today's maths lesson?"*

# Over the 10's

## Assessment focus

■ Can the children add or subtract crossing the 10's boundary?

## Resources

■ 1p and 10p coins

■ Resource sheets 2 and 13

■ place value cards

■ a 100 square

■ counters, cubes and dice

■ calculators

## With the whole class

■ Write a sum with a two-digit number added to a one-digit number so that the 10's boundary is crossed. Show how the answer can be found mentally by splitting the number to be added to make a two-stage operation, by making the answer up to the nearest multiple of 10 first.

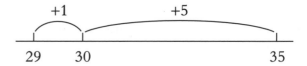

■ As a class work through several more examples of both addition and subtraction using this strategy and give the lower-achievers the opportunity to demonstrate how this can be done using an empty number line.

## With the lower-achievers

### With adult support

**Choose from:**

1   Hold up some pennies and a 10p. Count the amount together and circle the number on a number line. Count out some more pennies and a 10p, so that when the two amounts are added they cross the 10's boundary. Say that together you will find the total amount of money. Start with the first amount and add the pennies until 20 is reached, then add the 10p and count on the extra pennies. For example,

to find 16p + 17p: 16p + 10p = 26p, 26p + 4p = 30p and 30p + 3p = 33p

Show how to record this on an empty number line. Work through several more examples together, before giving the children some amounts of money to add in this way.

2   Give the children experience of drawing their own empty number lines and then using them to draw hops to represent their calculations. Use place value cards (use only units 5–9) to generate two-digit numbers and add 6, 7, 8 or 9 so that 10's will be crossed.

### Teacher-independent activities

**Choose from:**

1   Fill in Resource sheet 13 just with multiples of 10 as shown opposite. In turn two players throw a 1–9 dice and add or subtract the throw from one of the numbers on the board. The other player checks the answer using either a calculator or 100 square and if it is correct the number can be covered. The player with the most numbers covered is the winner.

2   As a continuation of the whole-class starter session, let the group use marked number lines and count on or back as required but encourage recording on an empty number line and going on or back to the nearest multiple of 10 as a strategy.

3   Ask the children to write as many additions and subtractions as they can with the answer 20. To get them started they could make a 'train' from 20 interlocking cubes and record what they make on Resource sheet 2.

## Plenary session

- ■ *"How many do I add to 25 to make 30?"*

- ■ *"I have got three coins in my hand. One coin is a 10p and the three coins add up to 25p. What are my coins?"*

- ■ *"I go shopping with 20p and spend 9p. How much change do I get?"*

- ■ Go over both addition and subtraction on number lines. Make the point that if the children are asked to show their workings (how they did it) for a calculation, a number line is ideal and they can draw these lines themselves.

# Finding the difference

## Assessment focus

- Can the children find the difference between a pair of numbers by counting on or back?

## Resources

- coins in purses
- cubes
- dice
- number cards and number lines
- Resource sheets 43, 45 and 46

## With the whole class

- Hold up two towers of interlocking cubes, one taller than the other and ask what the difference is between them. Some children may say that one is taller/shorter than the other but remind them that what is required is the number of cubes. Show how the 'difference' can be found by counting on along the cubes from the shorter to the longer and back. Then show this difference on a large 0–100 number line.

- Repeat this with other numbers of cubes. Ask two children to come to the front and, with large 0–9 cards, each make a two-digit number and then stand in the order the numbers appear on the line. Ask someone to show on the number line how to count forward from one to the next using hops of 10 where as possible. For example, using the numbers 29 and 45, this can be done as $29 + 1 = 30$, $30 + 10 = 40$ and $40 + 5 = 45$; so the difference is $1 + 10 + 5 = 16$.

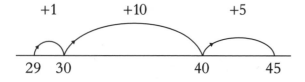

## With the lower-achievers

*With adult support*

**Choose from:**

1. Give each of the children a small purse (or a small envelope) containing a few coins. Ask each of them to count their money and write the amount on a white board. Discuss who has the most money and who has the least. How do they know? Tell them that you want them to work in pairs to find out who has the most/least and to think of a way to find the difference – this might be by matching coins, exchanging to all pennies and matching or using a number line. Discuss their strategies. Did anyone count on or back from one amount to the other? A simple way of recording is in three columns:

| My money | My friend's money | Difference |
|---|---|---|
| | | |
| | | |

2. Show the children how they can use a number line to find differences by counting on from the smaller to the larger number and checking by counting back.

3. Give the children copies of Resource sheet 45 but take care when using it for subtraction that you give the children plenty of experience with you, both counting on and counting back. Usually counting on is easier.

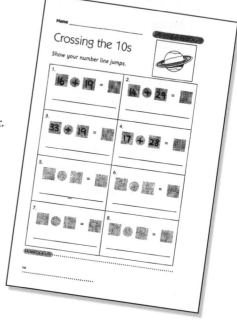

*Teacher-independent activities*

**Choose from:**

1  Use Resource sheet 43 by writing pairs of numbers with a difference of 5, for example. Cut the sheet into squares and ask the children to match the numbers with a difference of 5.

2  Working in twos or threes the children can play 'Difference pelmanism'. They use a set of 0–20 cards that are arranged face down on the table. Each player turns over two cards and if they make a difference of 5, for example, that player keeps the two cards. If the target difference is not made the cards are put face down again in the same position. Larger numbers or multiples of 10 can be used.

3  Use Resource sheet 46 for a track game for two players. The children take turns to throw two 1–10 dice. They find the difference between the two numbers and that is the size of their move. If the children have difficulty in finding the differences, suggest they use interlocking cubes or a number line. The winner has to score an exact difference to reach the finish line.

4  Ask the children to find as many pairs of numbers as they can with a difference of 5 (or any other suitable number). Encourage them to work systematically. This can be done by starting with a tower of 1 interlocking cube and another of 6 cubes, so 1 and 6 have a difference of 5. By adding one cube to each tower they find that 2 and 7 have a difference of 5 and so on. At a convenient time show the children how this can be done using a number line by counting on or back.

## Plenary session

- *"Can you explain how you would find the difference between 4 and 14?"*

- *"What is the difference between your age and your sister's?"*

- Play a difference game in two teams. The children take turns to take four number cards from a bag to make 2 two-digit numbers. The first team to call out the difference wins. A quieter game is for the two teams to compare their numbers and the team with the smaller number gets the chance to say what the difference is. If they are right they win 20 points. If not, the other team gets a chance.

# Multiplication and division

## Overall learning objectives

■ Understand the operation of multiplication as repeated addition and division as repeated subtraction.

....................................................
**Key words**

| | |
|---|---|
| lots of | addition/subtraction |
| groups of | divide |
| times | array |
| product | row and column |
| multiply | double |
| repeated | halve |
....................................................

# Doubles and halves
• • • • • • • • • • • • • • • • • • • • • • • •

## Assessment focus

■ Can the children understand that doubling is the same as multiplying by 2 and halving is the same as dividing by 2?

## Resources

■ cubes, counters, dice and coins

■ number cards and number lines

■ a large pot

■ Resource sheets 34, 47, 48, 49 and 60

## With the whole class

■ Tell the children a story about a special trick the alien can perform with his special machines that will double and halve numbers. Their task will be to see if they can do the trick too.

■ Draw two function machines on the board saying which one doubles numbers and which one halves them. Ask a child to write a one- or two-digit number on the board and ask what happens if it goes into the doubling machine. Everyone shows the answer with their number cards. Discuss the methods they used. *"Now the doubled number is going into the halving machine. Show me the new answer."*

■ Try several examples. Can the children explain what happens when numbers are first doubled and then halved? Select some numbers that can first be halved and then doubled to demonstrate how the operations are the inverse of each other.

■ Explain how to use the doubling and halving machines on Resource sheet 49. They should use 1–9 cards to get the start number. This is doubled and then halved to help develop an understanding that these are inverse operations.

## With the lower-achievers

*With adult support*

**Choose from:**

1 Show the group a large, interesting looking pot or use the function machine from Chapter 3 and say that it is a very special pot because it can double everything that is put into it. So if they put in 2 cubes, 4 will come out and 6 pennies will become 12, and so on. Show practically how things can be doubled by counting out the number of cubes, for example, and counting out the same number again to find the total. Show calculation on the number line.

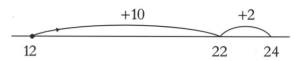

*"This shows 12 x 2."*

2 Help the children to memorise doubles of numbers to 5, then 10, then 20. Start using fingers to show, for example *"Double 3 is 6."* Make sure they understand 'double' as '2 lots of' or 'the same number again'. To help them to memorise, go over the numbers many times. For example, ask *"What is double 3? – 2, 4, 1, 5, 4, 5, 4, 5, 2?"* and so on. Repeat this with numbers to 10 and beyond, then go over these doubles every day in mental maths time for at least two weeks.

*Teacher-independent activities*

**Choose from:**

1   On Resource sheet 47, the children have to buy two of everything. Let them choose coins to help. You could make more sheets like this using items from Resource sheet 60.

2   Give the children copies of Resource sheet 48. Here they have to halve the prices.

3   Using cubes, ask the children to find the doubles of all the numbers from 1 to 10 and make a list of them. Working in pairs, they can use 1–10 cards that have been shuffled and placed face down on the table. In turn, each turns over a card and says the double without looking at the list. Their partner can look at the list and say if the answer is right. If it is, a point is scored.

4   Resource sheet 49 can be done in pairs. The children can use 1–9 cards or a dice to get their start numbers.

5   Use Resource sheet 34 to play a 'Three in a row' game in pairs to do some doubling and halving. See the example below. Use the circle as a spinner or just choose whether to double or halve.

## Plenary session

■   *"What happens when you double a number and then halve the answer?"*

■   *"Who knows all their doubles to 10?"*

■   Play 'Double my number'. In teams, the children take it in turns to take a number card and quickly call out the double. You can play where one team calls out the double, or two teams race to call out – but that is noisy!

■   *"What does 'double' mean? Which times table is used for doubling?"*

# Rectangle patterns

## Assessment focus

■   Can the children use and describe multiplication arrays?

## Resources

■   a pegboard and pegs, dice and cubes

■   number cards, egg boxes and other arrays

■   Resource sheet 15

■   number lines

■   bun tins, card of buttons and plastic eggs

## With the whole class

■   Give each pair of children or individuals 12 cubes and ask them to make a rectangle (without any spaces in the middle). Invite pairs to show their rectangles and ask questions like, *"How many in each row?"*, *"If you turn it how many are in each row now?"* and *"Has anyone a different rectangle with the same number of cubes?"* Ask the children if any numbers could only make one row. (All numbers can make one row.) Show how the arrays can be recorded in pictures and using words and symbols, for example 4 rows of 3, 3 + 3 + 3 + 3, 3 x 4 and so on. Show how the rectangle arrays can be looked at in two ways; 4 x 3 and 3 x 4.

# With the lower-achievers

*With adult support*

**Choose from:**

1 Provide the group with some egg boxes, baking tins for small cakes, cards of buttons and so on – anything that has arrays. Start with an egg box and all count together as either plastic eggs or cubes are placed in each space. Talk about the way the eggs are arranged in rows and columns, counting the number in each row and column. Show how this can be written as

> 3 rows of 2 make 6

and it can also be written as

> $2 + 2 + 2 = 6$
>
> $2 \times 3 = 6$
>
> $3 + 3 = 6$ and
>
> $3 \times 2 = 6$.

Then ask a child to show this as hops along a number line, stressing that the hops are all the same size. Give each pair one of the resources. Ask them to describe the array to the others in the group and to write the calculations in as many ways as they can.

2 Many lower-achievers, when asked to make '3 rows of 4', will put 3 cubes and another 4. So, you need to check that every child can use the language of 'lots of', 'rows of', 'groups of' and so on appropriately. Give each child their own task, such as *"Make 6 lots of 3"* or *"3 lots of 3"* or *"8 lots of 3"* and so on. Then let them describe in turn their arrays, using a range of language, such as 'rows', 'columns' and 'lots of'. If they are not clear about what they are doing, put out cubes showing $2 + 5$ and $2 \times 5$ and ask *"Which is 2 lots of 5?"*

*Teacher-independent activities*

**Choose from:**

1 Give pairs of children a pegboard and pegs and two 1–6 dice. They throw the two dice and use the numbers to make rectangular arrays; so if 3 and 5 are thrown they make a 3 x 5 rectangle. This is recorded by drawing and writing the numbers in each row, which in this example will be '3 rows of 5 make 15' and also '5 rows of 3 make 15'. The dice are thrown again to get another array.

2 Using Resource sheet 15, let the children cut the stamps into rectangular arrays, stick them in their books and write number sentences to show the numbers in the rows and columns.

3 Give the children some interlocking cubes and some cards with even numbers between 2 and 20 written on them. In pairs they should take a number and make as many arrays as they can with that number of cubes. The arrays can be drawn on squared paper.

## Plenary session

- *"You have cut your stamps into four rows with five stamps in each row. Can you write that as an addition on the board?"*

- *"Which numbers did you find would only make a single row?"* (For example, prime numbers, 3, 5, 7, 11, 13, 17 and 19.)

- *"Which of your numbers had the largest number of different arrays?"* (For example, 12 and 24.)

- *"Iqbal, come and make 3 lots of 2 with these cubes."*

- Hold up baking tins and egg boxes and ask for a description of the array.

- *"What have you learned today about multiplication?"*

# Adding again and again

## Assessment focus

- Can the children use a repeated addition or subtraction for multiplication and division?

## Resources

- card or felt shapes (triangles, squares) and paper circles
- model cars
- counters, cubes and dice
- Resource sheet 31
- a number line and number cards in a bag

## With the whole class

You might want to cover the two different aspects of division (grouping and sharing) on two different days, then do a day on both aspects.

- Use an animal (or alien) of your choice with the number of legs you want to work with, for example chicks for x 2, cats for x 4, bugs for x 6 or spiders for x 8.

- Draw one animal on the board. Together count the legs and write the multiplication. For example, for a cat write 4 x 1. Draw a second cat, counting the legs of this cat and then both together. Write the calculation 4 + 4 and also 4 x 2 . Continue until there are 10 cats.

- Show that $4 + 4 + 4 + 4 + 4 + 4 + 4 + 4 + 4 + 4 = 40$ can be written as $4 \times 10 = 40$ and explain that this is a shorter way of writing the same calculation. Ask one of the children to draw the multiples of 4 on the number line.

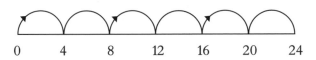

- Emphasise that multiplication is the same as adding the same number over and over again.

- Demonstrate that if there are 10 cats (40 legs), $40 \div 10 = 4$ shows the inverse operation.

## With the lower-achievers

*With adult support*

**Choose from:**

1   Display a number line. Say *"If I give everyone a cube, how many cubes do I need?"* Give everyone a cube to check the number and ask someone to mark this as a jump from 0 on the number line. Continue by asking how many are needed to give another cube to everyone and draw the hop along the number line. Continue giving out the cubes and marking the hops. Count the sequence of numbers that have been hopped on and ask how many more each time and how they know. Ask a child to write this as an addition sentence (for example, $4 + 4 + 4 + 4 = 16$).

2   Show on the number line how taking away 4's from 16 is the same as equal subtraction or $16 \div 4 = 4$, $12 \div 4 = 3$ and so on. Refer to the practical grouping of the cubes in 4's.

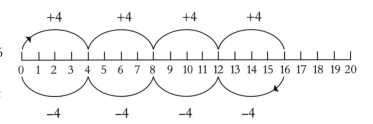

Give other examples, such as *"There are 12 cubes in a 'train'. If you break off the carriages in 3's, this means you will end up with 4 lots of 3."* Again, show this on a number line.

3   Set up some 'grouping' stories, where there is no equal sharing. For example, *"The teacher has 12 apples. To how many children can she give 2?"* (Six children and some children might get none.)

*Teacher-independent activities*

**Choose from:**

1   Give some of the children a card or felt square with some cubes and give others a triangle. Ask them to put the same number of cubes on each corner of their shape and find the total number of cubes each time and record this in a drawing.

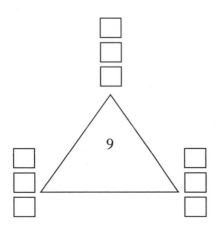

Another example of their drawing might be:

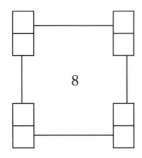

At the end of the lesson ask the children to explain to the class what number pattern they were counting in. (So with triangles they will have the x 3 pattern, 3, 6, 9 and so on.) Ask one of the group to show this on a number line.

2   From a collection of model cars ask the children to take a small selection. Tell them to count the wheels in groups of 4 and show this on a number line as equal jumps of 4. The children could draw their cars and write the number sentences to show equal addition.

3   The group needs some paper circles (pretend plates) and some counters (cakes). In pairs, they throw a dice and they take that many 'plates'.

Then they throw the dice again. This is the number of 'cakes' they will put on each 'plate'. Ask them to draw pictures of the plates of cakes with the equal addition and multiplication number sentences.

4   Use paper circles and cakes again but this time share out the cakes equally. Mark the four faces of a Unifix cube 2, 3, 4 and 5. This is thrown as a dice to give the number of plates. (If the cube lands on the top or bottom they just throw again.) Then a number card is taken from a bag (use numbers 4, 6, 8, 9, 12 and 15 or numbers to suit your children) to show the number of cakes. If the cakes can be shared into equal groups on the plates, they win a point.

5   Pairs of children play 'Collecting fives' using Resource sheet 31. Fill in the sheet with some of the spaces having pictures of 5p coins. The aim is to collect 10 x 5p coins. The children choose a space to start on then throw the dice and move that number of spaces with the aim of landing on a circle containing a 5p coin. Scores can be recorded as equal addition of 5's and then compared.

# Plenary session

■   *"You had 3 plates with 5 cakes on each of them, so how many cakes was that altogether? Can you think of a quick way to count them?"*

■   *"Well done! You have found a Lego brick with an array. Can you tell everyone about it?"*

■   *"If I give you 3 cakes, Billy 2 cakes and Lizzy 4 cakes, have I shared them equally?"*

■   *"If you have 15 cakes to share, what would be a good number of plates to have?"*

■   Play the plates and cakes game in two teams.

■   Give more 'grouping' problems. For example, *"At the party, there are 10 buns. How many children could have 2 each?"* (5 but some children might not get any.) Point out that dividing like this is different from sharing out the 10 buns equally.

# Fractions

## Overall learning objectives

- Recognise fractions, such as halves, quarters and eighths and use them to find fractions of numbers.

### Key words

| | |
|---|---|
| equal parts | quarter/third/fifth/ |
| one whole | tenth |
| one half | fraction |
| one | same number |
| | same fractions |

# Splitting equally

## Assessment focus

- Can the children find fractions of shapes and numbers and explain their work?

## Resources

- pretend biscuits
- number lines and number cards
- cubes, buttons, beads, ribbon, string, paper bags and counters
- paper shapes, particularly circles
- fraction game boards, tiles and dice
- Resource sheets 13, 31, 50, 51 and 52

## With the whole class

(You might want to do fractions of shapes and numbers on different days.)

- Ask eight children to stand in front of the class. Ask how many children make half of the total. How do they work this out? How many make a quarter? What other fraction can be made? Talk about the same number of children being in each fraction. For example, with halves there are four in each half, with quarters there are two and so on.

- Ask each group to take 24 cubes and make as many different fractions as possible, starting with halves, and write them down. (*"Today we will be making fractions and no-one is allowed to cut any cubes in half!"*) After a few minutes ask them to share the fractions and write them on the board. They should find a half, a third, a quarter, a sixth, an eighth and a twelfth. Stress the importance of the number in each fraction always being the same. Pose questions such as *"How many cubes make two quarters?", "What fraction is that the same as?", "How many in two sixths?"* and *"Why didn't it work to find a fifth of 24?"*

## With the lower-achievers

*With adult support*

**Choose from:**

1. Make up a story about an alien needing the group's help. She has some biscuits (or balloons or flags) and wants to know what fractions she can make. Draw her face on a large sheet of paper. Say that she has 12 biscuits and what fractions can she make? Can she split the number in half and if so can they suggest how it is done? Give the children some counters or pretend biscuits. Write '$\frac{1}{2}$ of 12 is 6' on the paper. Talk about splitting the number in two equal groups. Ask what others they can make and add these to the paper, such as $\frac{1}{4}$ of 12 is 3. Talk about the number in $\frac{2}{4}$ or in $\frac{3}{4}$. Add these answers to the paper with the alien's face on it. Thirds and sixths can also be found. Choose some other numbers, such as 20, which can be halved and quartered easily. Stress the point that what they are doing is the same as dividing numbers of biscuits equally, without cutting any into smaller pieces.

2. Do some paper folding/cutting/colouring perhaps with the aim of making a paper 'patchwork quilt'. Make halves, quarters and so on. (See the examples on page 47.)

3. Give the children a 'good' number for finding fractions, such as 12, 18 or 24, and ask them to use that many cubes to find a half and a quarter. Point out that with 9 you can't make half in each group with cubes because you can't cut cubes into bits. So for this activity we say you

can't find half of 9. Of course, if you wanted to find half of 9 cookies, you could because you could cut them into halves. Ask the children to record in their own way, drawing their cubes and practising writing the symbols for a half and a quarter. Extend the activity by finding thirds and fifths. (You or they should choose appropriate numbers for this.) Later, extend the task by recording on Resource sheet 51.

4   Start with some strips of ribbon or string and ask the children to show you how to find half. Expect them to do this by folding. If they fold the length in half again, can they say the fraction and the number of equal parts? Ask them to mark the divisions in some way. What happens if the lengths are folded in half again? How many pieces are there? Together name the fractions. Use equal length strips of paper and repeat the folding so the children each end up with a fraction set of a whole, halves, quarters and eighths. To develop understanding of equivalent fractions, ask questions about how many quarters are the same as a half or a whole.

### Teacher-independent activities

### Choose from:

1   Give the group collections of small objects in little bags, such as buttons, beads and centicubes. These can be counted and the children asked to find half of each collection by dividing it into two equal sets. Use paper circles for them to show the half sets and then draw them. Can they put any collections into quarters by dividing into four equal sets?

2   Provide some number cards with even numbers only. Choose numbers appropriate for the group. Ask them each to choose a number card and to make a 'train' using that number of interlocking cubes in two colours. The 'trains' should be half one colour and half the second colour. Using the same 'train' the children should rearrange the two colours so that the fraction is the same although the arrangement is not.

3   Tell a story about the alien's planet needing a new flag and say that you have some squares and triangles of material in two colours to make

it. The alien says the flags must be half one colour and half another colour, so can the children find some different designs for her to choose from? They can use Resource sheet 50 for recording.

4   Cut Resource sheet 52 into squares. The children should work in pairs or as a whole group to match the fractions to put the puzzle back together again.

5   Use Resource sheet 31 filled in like this.

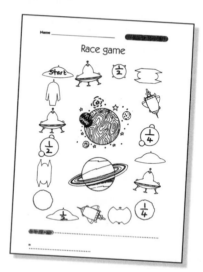

You need a 1–6 dice, a counter each and lots of paper $\frac{1}{2}$ and $\frac{1}{4}$ circles. Take turns to throw the dice and move in any direction. If you land on a $\frac{1}{2}$ or a $\frac{1}{4}$, take a piece of circle that size. The first to collect 5 whole circles is the winner.

6   Use Resource sheet 13 filled in like this.

You need two players, a dice marked $\frac{1}{2}, \frac{1}{2}, \frac{1}{2}, \frac{1}{4}$, $\frac{1}{4}, \frac{1}{4}$, a set of counters each and the number cards for 4, 8, 12, 16, 20 and 24. Shuffle the cards and put them face down on the table. The first player turns over a card, throws the dice and works out the fraction, for example $\frac{1}{2}$ of 20. If the second player agrees, the answer (10) is covered with a counter. The winner is the first player to get three in a row.

## Plenary session

- *"Can you tell everyone how you could find half of 10?"*

- *"Do you have more cookies if you have $\frac{1}{2}$ of 12 or if you have $\frac{1}{4}$ of 12?"*

- *"If I split 10 cookies into 2 groups, 4 and 6, will each group be half? Why not?"*

- *"We said we couldn't find half of 9 cubes. If they were 9 cookies shared between 2 people, how many would they have each?"*

- Using paper fraction strips give some equivalent fractions for the children to demonstrate to the rest of the class.

# Where does it go?

## Assessment focus

- Can the children position fractions on a number line?

## Resources

- number lines and number cards (including fractions)
- paper strips

## With the whole class

- Draw a 0–20 number line on the board, spacing the numbers out. Point to two consecutive numbers and ask someone to write the number that goes between them, for example between 5 and 6 they write $5\frac{1}{2}$. With the children's help fill in all the half numbers up to 20 and say

them together. Can they continue the counting up to 50 or beyond? Ask *"What is between 125 and 126?"*

- Point to the space between 6 and $6\frac{1}{2}$ asking if they know what will go there. Expect some children to be able to explain that $\frac{1}{4}$ is $\frac{1}{2}$ of a $\frac{1}{2}$. So if $6\frac{1}{4}$ goes between 6 and $6\frac{1}{2}$, what comes between $6\frac{1}{2}$ and 7? Ask which is more, $\frac{1}{4}$ or $\frac{1}{2}$, and how they know. Say together all the numbers between 0 and 10, including halves and quarters.

- Count in halves from 0 to 20.

## With the lower-achievers

### *With adult support*

**Choose from:**

1  With the children's help, draw a 0–10 number line with the numbers well spaced out. Give out some strips of paper and ask the group to fold them in two. Ask *"What fraction have you made?"* Get one child to write 0 at one end of their strip and 1 at the other end. Can anyone say and write the number that comes halfway? Ask another child to write 1 and 2 at either end of their strip. Again, write in the halfway number. Continue to the number between 9 and 10. Write all the halves on the number line and then say the numbers together. *"With your strip of paper can you show $\frac{3}{4}$?"*

2  Display a 0–20 number line and point to two consecutive numbers between 10 and 20. Ask the children what comes between those two numbers. Write all the whole and half numbers to 20 and say them together forwards and backwards. Can they say what comes between 21 and 22, for example, and give a reason for their answer?

### *Teacher-independent activities*

**Choose from:**

1  Give the children some number lines, with the numbers spaced out, and some cards with fractions written on them. So, if they have a 0–20 number line the cards might be $3\frac{1}{2}$ and $8\frac{1}{2}$. The children should write the fractions in their correct places on the number line.

2 Provide a set of 0–9 number cards including all the halves. In pairs the children should discuss the position of each as they try to put the cards in order as quickly as possible.

## Plenary session

- ◼ *"Can you show where 5¼ comes on the number line?"*

- ◼ *"What have your learned today about fractions?"*

- ◼ *"Is there anything that still confuses you about fractions?"*

- ◼ Do a paper folding demonstration, for example folding a circle into halves and so on.

# Practical fractions

## Assessment focus

- ◼ Can the children use simple fractions in a practical situation?

## Resources

- ◼ Plasticene

- ◼ balances

- ◼ collections of small objects in bags

- ◼ cubes and fractions dice

- ◼ paper squares, rectangles and circles

- ◼ chocolate bar playing board (such as the one below)

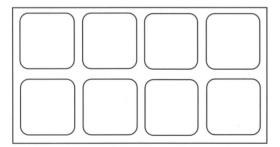

## With the whole class

- ◼ Give the children some rectangles of paper in several different sizes. Talk about this being one whole shape. Ask them to fold it exactly in half. Ask *"How many pieces are there?"* and *"Has everyone made two equal pieces?"* Stress the fact that when looking at two halves both pieces will be exactly the same size because it is just like dividing by 2. Can anyone write the fraction for a half? Fold the papers again. How many pieces are there now and are they all the same size? Ask *"Who can write a quarter?", "Which is larger, a half or a quarter?"* and *"If you fold the paper again what fraction will you get this time? What makes you think that?"* Can the children comment on the fraction pattern of $\frac{1}{2}$, $\frac{1}{4}$, $\frac{1}{8}$, $\frac{1}{16}$ … and explain why $\frac{1}{16}$ is so much smaller than $\frac{1}{2}$?

- ◼ Show the children a large piece of Plasticene and a balance. Can they suggest how the Plasticene can be divided exactly in half? Demonstrate how to use the balance as accurately as possible.

## With the lower-achievers

*With adult support*

**Choose from:**

1 Present the scenario that the group is to prepare a picnic for the class. Ideally give them real bread and fillings, otherwise they can use squares of white paper. Show how they can be cut into quarters along the diagonals. Some rectangles in a different colour can represent four-finger chocolate biscuits and can be cut accordingly.

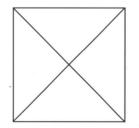 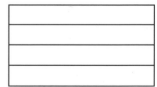

Ask the group to work in pairs and find out how many whole sandwiches and chocolate bars will be needed if everyone has three one-quarter pieces of sandwich and one chocolate finger. In pairs the children can work out the numbers needed for each group in the class.

2   With paper squares all the same size (about 12cm square is ideal), construct a series of patchwork quilts. Ask the children to fold their squares very carefully in half and then in half again, finding as many different ways to fold them as possible. Observe – who can identify halves, quarters and three-quarters? To make three different quilts, each child needs at least three folded squares. One they colour half blue, another half yellow and the third half red. They then lay out the halves together to make a blue and white quilt, and so on.

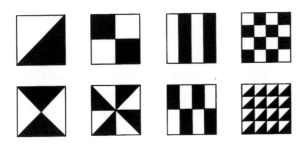

3   With paper circles representing pizzas or cakes, set a problem such as *"Everyone in this group wants to eat three-quarters of a pizza. How many pizzas do we need?"* Observe – who can give appropriate names to one quarter, one half and three-quarters?

### *Teacher-independent activities*

### Choose from:

1   Play the 'Chocolate bar fractions' game. Two players each need a 'chocolate bar' playing board, with some cubes to cover each of the eighths, and a dice marked $\frac{1}{2}, \frac{1}{2}, \frac{1}{4}, \frac{1}{4}, \frac{1}{8}, \frac{1}{8}$. In turn the players throw the dice and cover on the bar the fraction shown on the dice. The exact fraction must be thrown to win the game. Repeat the game by removing the number of cubes each time as though the chocolate is being eaten. Play the two games several times.

2   Ask the group to start by drawing and cutting out three sausages of the same size each. Tell them that they have to find a way to share the three 'sausages' between four children. How much sausage will each child have? Continue by using five, then six sausages. They should record this by sticking the amount of sausage for each child on paper and writing the fractions.

3   The group needs a collection of things that can be halved. The collection might include different shaped pieces of paper, fruit, vegetables, scissors, balls, a bag of counters and a pot of butter-beans. The group can discuss and explore different ways of dividing into two.

## Plenary session

■   *"When you were playing the 'Chocolate bar fractions' game which was the best fraction to throw? Why was that?"*

■   *"Can you tell everyone how many sandwiches you needed for your group? How did you work it out?"*

■   *"When you found half a circle did you use the same way as finding half the jar of beans?"*

■   *"What do you think you could call each bit of a cake if you cut the cake into 100 pieces all the same size?"*

■   *"Look carefully at the blue and white squares. What can you tell me about them?"* Make the point that they are all one half blue but some halves are coloured in different ways. Set a challenge. *"Take a square and colour one half blue in a way that no-one else has done."*

# Solving problems and money

## Overall learning objectives

- Choose and use appropriate operations and calculation strategies to solve problems, explaining how the problems were solved.

> **Key words**
>
> total amount     method
> value     operation
> costs more     sign
> how much change?     symbol

# What's the problem?

## Assessment focus

- Can the children explain their solutions to a variety of problems?

## Resources

- money – real if possible
- large cardboard coins such as Mega Money from BEAM
- a coin poster
- 2cm interlocking cubes
- tubes of different coloured wrapped sweets, such as Starbursts
- plastic cups and a litre bottle of coloured water
- Resource sheets 53 and 60
- marbles, cotton reels, balances and weights

## With the whole class

You might want to do the different aspects of this chapter on different days.

- Demonstrate using a balance, making sure that all the children know that the heavier object will make the balance go down. Let the children hold two items in their hands to do some direct weight comparisons and then check their findings on the balances.

- Set some small tasks for the children to solve in pairs, such as three children sharing 10 buns. How many might each child get if they can cut up the buns?

- Demonstrate simple capacity. For example, *"Guess how many cupfuls of water are in this bottle."* Write up the children's guesses and then find out the answer by measuring.

## With the lower-achievers

### With adult support

**Choose from:**

1 Give the children copies of Resource sheet 53. This involves finding out how many of the different objects will balance a 50g weight. Show them how 2 x 50g will balance 100g; so if 6 wooden cubes balance 50g, how many will balance 100g? Talk about the need to double the numbers.

2 Using Resource sheet 60 (money clip art) with some prices filled in, enlarge and cut out some items and set up a shopping situation. Observe – who is confident with adding amounts and giving change?

### Teacher-independent activities

**Choose from:**

1 Give pairs of children a packet of different coloured wrapped sweets. Tell them to open the packets and count how many there are of each colour. If they had 5 packets exactly the same, how many of each colour would there be altogether? The children can use interlocking cubes to model the number of each colour. Can they find a way to record what they did?

2 Give the group some plastic cups and a litre bottle of coloured water. Say that their task is to find how many cupfuls they can pour from a bottle. Tell them to talk about how full each cup needs to be to make it fair. Once they have found that information say they are going to try to find out how many bottles are needed to give everyone in the class a cup of drink. Tell them to plan what to say in the plenary session about how they solved this problem.

## Plenary session

- *"If you made 6 drinks from one bottle, how many could you make from 2 bottles?"*

- *"If you need £10 to buy a football and you have £6 saved up, how much more must you save?"*

- *"So if there were 3 red sweets in a packet, how many would be in 5 packets? How did you work it out?"*

# Number stories

## Assessment focus

- Can the children solve problems and write number stories to reflect practical situations?

## Resources

- Resource sheets 54 and 55
- plastic clocks
- coins
- small boxes and cubes
- toys, sweets and so on
- counters and paper circles

## With the whole class

- Tell a word number story about some children going to the cinema to see a space film with their family. As you go along, ask some children to write the sentences on the board. Discuss the type of operation they need to use and some of the words that give us a clue. For example, you could say that 2 children go to the cinema and that one has a bag of 15 sweets, the other a bag of 12 sweets. Ask how many altogether. The key facts are:

  2 children with 15 sweets and 12 sweets with 'altogether' giving the clue.

  However, if you ask how many more sweets Toby has than Sam, the clue is in the 'how many more'. Try some simple examples like this to help the children think through the type of operation needed.

- Try a longer but simpler story, such as *"Kim and Katie went to the cinema with their mum, dad and gran. So how many people were there?", "It cost £3/£3.50 for an adult. How much did they pay for the adults?", "Tickets for children cost £2. How much did the family pay altogether?", "The 2 children met 4 friends. They all had popcorn which cost 50p each. How much was that?"* and *"The film started at 6.30pm and lasted for 2 hours. What time did it end?"*

## With the lower-achievers

### With adult support

### Choose from:

1  Give the children some small boxes containing different numbers of coloured cubes. (Stock cube boxes are ideal as they come in several sizes and hold 2cm cubes.) Ask each person to count their cubes, make a note of the number and how many of each colour there are. See if the children can suggest a number sentence to write about their collection of cubes. For example, *"Aziz has 3 red, 3 yellow and 4 blue cubes. How many is that?"* Let each child write their sentence and discuss what other questions they could ask, such as *"How many more has Billy than Jane?"* Try to give examples of different operations; *"If you shared your cubes with a friend, how many would each of you have?"* or *"If you had 2 boxes full, how many would that be?"* Each time discuss the key words that help them decide on the operation.

2  Give the children copies of Resource sheet 55. The problems involve different types of calculation. The numbers are fairly easy because the main focus is on the children recognising the operation needed to solve the problem. For the last question they might need to be given a context and some practical equipment for writing a story using a pair of numbers.

3  Say that Varn, the alien, has made 20 chocolate cookies. He wants to share them equally with other aliens. How many ways can he share them so that they each have the same number? To start them off say that there were 20 aliens. How many would they have each? Suggest they use counters as cookies and paper circles as plates. Tell them to write some number sentences to show what they have done.

*Teacher-independent activities*

**Choose from:**

1 Give the children copies of Resource sheet 54. This will give them some experience in answering number story questions and help them to think about a similar story they could write. Get each child to write their number story question and give it to a friend to answer.

2 Encourage the children to write more stories using the prices on Resource sheet 54.

3 Set up another story situation, for example about a barbecue. Write crucial information on the board.

| Starts 6.30pm | Ends 8pm |
|---|---|
| burgers | 35p |
| hot dogs | 30p |
| coke | 40p |
| juice | 25p |

The children should write number stories for this. For example, '3 friends went to the barbecue and they bought …' or 'Tom had £2.50 to spend at the barbecue and he …'

## Plenary session

- *"How would you work out the number of pencils I would need to give 1 to each of the children on those two tables?"*

- *"Supposing I give 3 cakes to everyone on your table, how would I work out how many I need?"*

- Go over the key words that indicate the type of calculation to use to solve a problem.

- *"What key words did you use in your barbecue story?"*

# Money problems

## Assessment focus

- Can the children solve problems using money?

## Resources

- small items, such as pencil-sharpeners, toys and lollipops with prices on them

- coins and purses/bags,

- circles, squares, isosceles and equilateral triangles and rectangles, all with prices written on them

- Resource sheets 46, 56, 57, 59 and 60

- money poster and dice

## With the whole class

- Make a display of toys with price tags and put some money on each table (or use Resource sheet 60). Hold up one of the toys and ask each table to find a way of paying for it using the coins on their table. Encourage them to discuss the options in their group and then ask someone from each group to stand up and say what they did. Write on the board the different solutions and talk about the ways chosen.

- Ask each group to work out the change they will receive from a given amount of money. For example, *"Blue group, you have £4."* Hold up a toy, and ask the group to work out their change after buying it. Ask how they worked out the answer and which coins they used. Show them the shopkeepers' method of calculating the change by counting on to find the difference.

- Tell each group they have £10 to spend and they can buy 2 of the toys. What is their change? Again, they share what they did with the class.

- Pose problems, such as *"A kite costs 3 silver coins. What price could the kite be?"* Talk about the different silver coins we have in our currency. Agree the different amounts the kite could cost and write them on the board, for example 15p, 30p, 60p and £1.50.

■ Say *"A hat costs £5.95."* Discuss the coins or notes that could have been used to pay for this. Extend with questions like, *"If the hat was paid for with only silver coins, what would they be?"* and *"What is the smallest/largest number of coins?"*

## With the lower-achievers

### With adult support

**Choose from:**

1   Put a pile of mixed coins on the table. Hold up each type of coin in turn and ask its value. Can the children make the same amount in different ways? Start with 10p and compare the different ways they used. Write these on a board. Put out some toys or small items with prices on. Choose one and ask how much it is and then ask the children to find coins to pay for it. Have they all done this the same way? Discuss their solutions. After this has been done with several items hold up one of them again. Give each child some money that is more than the cost of the item. Ask how much they have and say *"If you bought the toy alien for 45p, how much change would you need from your 60p?"* Show them how they can work out the difference by counting on. *"So if the toy alien cost 45p, 5p more makes 50p and 10p more makes 60p. That makes your change 15p."*

2   Give each child one of the toys and a purse containing more money than is needed to pay for the toy. Ask them to count their money and work out the change needed and then to find the coins needed for change. This can be recorded informally.

### Teacher-independent activities

**Choose from:**

1   Give the children Resource sheet 56. This shows the coins the children might use to make the amounts shown in the money chests. Suggest they find the coins first and place them on the chests before drawing or writing on the sheet.

2   Give the group a collection of shapes with a price list similar to the one below. Ask them to make an alien picture using as many of the shapes as they want and find out how much it costs to make. Compare the costs of each alien. How would a more expensive one be made?

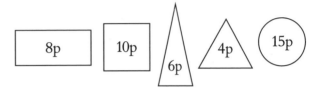

3   Have ready a small poster showing the group the coins they can use and some small toys with price labels attached. Tell the children that they are to choose one of the toys and work out different ways of paying for it using the coins shown on the poster. Make coins available for the children to use and draw round for recording.

4   Give the children copies of Resource sheet 57 which gives practice at addition and subtraction using pounds and working within £12. The group will need 50p and £1 coins.

5   Have prepared Resource sheet 46 to use as a money game. Fill in some of the spaces with 'Spend 10p', 'Mum gives you 5p', 'You lose 15p', 'Buy a lolly for 5p', 'You find 20p' and so on. This will help the children to make practical use of money for addition and subtraction. Explain that they start the game with 25p, throw a dice, then either add to it or subtract from it depending on what it says on the square they land on. To help them, list the vocabulary that they need and the operation each relates to. For example, 'spend' means 'subtract'.

## Plenary session

■ *"If you have £10 and buy a toy for £8, how much change will you get?"*

■ *"Grandma gives you 50p and Mum gives you 40p. How much have you altogether?"*

■ Tell more number stories, clarifying the number operation that is needed.

■ *"Lisa, tell us a number story that uses adding."*

■ *"Which key words for adding did Lisa use?"*

# Measurement

## Overall learning objectives

- Make reasonable estimates of length, mass and capacity and suggest appropriate units for measuring.

- Compare and order several items using their measurements and develop an understanding of the relationship between units.

> **Key words**
>
> | | |
> |---|---|
> | measure | heavy/light |
> | compare | weigh |
> | estimate | balance |
> | nearly | full/empty |
> | about the same | all the units of |
> | tall/short | measures |

# How long?

## Assessment focus

- Can the children suggest appropriate units for measuring length and work with increasing accuracy?

## Resources

- metre sticks, rulers, tape measures, height measure, surveyors' tapes and trundle wheel

- 1cm and 2cm squared and plain paper

- lengths of ribbon, string, paper and so on

## With the whole class

- Go over metric units explaining the 10's, 100's and 1000's. For example, there are 100cm in a metre. You could write these up on the wall, gradually adding other units, and use the chart you make as a basis for mental maths for a few weeks.

- Show a selection of length measuring tools, including a surveyor's tape and trundle wheel. Write their names on the board. Ask the class to suggest what each could be used to measure and write the suggestions under the word.

| Ruler | Metre stick | Tape measure | Surveyor's tape |
|---|---|---|---|
| foot | our height | around our heads | playground |
| books | classroom height | classroom windows | hall |

Discuss the units that each piece of equipment is best suited for measuring and when they might use a combination of equipment. So, for measuring a long jump they might use a metre stick and a tape measure for the extra bits. Remind the children about measuring to the nearest centimetre or half centimetre.

## With the lower-achievers

*With adult support*

**Choose from:**

1 Put a collection of measuring tools out. Let the group handle the equipment. Ask them to look at the numbers to see how far apart they are and which numbers have been used. Focus their attention on the metres and centimetres, letting them compare centimetres on a ruler with those on a metre stick and a height measure, and so on. Tell them they are going to measure their own heights and ask which equipment they could use for this. Say they must be very accurate – talk about measuring to the nearest centimetre – and must work together to do the measuring. When they have finished, check the accuracy of their work. Let the group write their names and their heights on a large sheet of paper, recording as centimetres. Show how they are all 1m and so many centimetres tall and how this can be written as m and cm. Together put the heights in order, talking about tallest/shortest and the number of centimetres difference between the heights. *"How many*

*centimetres taller than Josie is Ted?"* Measure full arm spans in the same way and compare the measurements with their heights.

2   Discuss with the children how they would measure the height of the classroom. Which equipment and measuring units would be best? They could do this by measuring the height of a child. For example, *"Josh is 156cm tall, so that can be rounded up to 160cm. About two and a half of Josh's height would be the approximate height of the classroom. That is 160cm + 160cm + 80cm = 400cm = 4m."*

3.  Ask the children to imagine they are clowns on stilts and say that together they will be finding out what height of stilts they would need for their heads to touch the ceiling. In pairs, the children measure their heights, then together do the calculation to find the height of stilts needed using an empty number line. *"Josh is 156cm tall and the classroom is 750cm high."* This could be done as 156cm + 4cm = 160cm, then counting up in 10's until they reach 250cm.

### *Teacher-independent activities*

### Choose from:

1   Ask the children to cut a piece of string the same length as their height and measure it. Challenge them, by folding and measuring the string, to find their height if they had shrunk to half as tall or a quarter as tall. Using doubling they could find their height if they grew twice as tall.

2   Tell the group that they are going to find out how much longer their foot is than their hand span and that they must decide which is the best equipment to use from the range available. Each child in the group draws around their hand span (with the help of a partner) and their foot, then cuts them out. They measure both to the nearest half centimetre, writing the measurements on the cut-outs. The difference in measurements can be found either by using a number line or measuring, or for some it might only be appropriate to use direct comparison.

## Plenary session

■   Ask some of the group to explain their strategy for working out the height of stilts they would need.

■   *"Which person would need the longest stilts?"*

■   *"Did the tallest person need the longest stilts?"*

# Weighing things up

## Assessment focus

■   Can the children use a balance to compare and order weights?

## Resources

■   balances with 1g, 10g, 100g 250g, 500g and 1kg weights

■   objects for weighing large and small amounts – paper clips, polystyrene packing, rice and counters

■   cubes and centicubes

■   place value cards

■   commercially produced cans and packages showing the weights

■   a collection of parcels and a parcel postage list from the Post Office

■   Resource sheet 58

■   apple, shoe, cup and book

## With the whole class

■   Display a balance and a variety of gram weights. Remind the class how the balance is used to find the weight of something and ask someone to demonstrate by weighing something on their table. Discuss which would be the best weights to use for a particular purpose. For example, *"Which will I use to weigh a brick?"* Hold up the 1 kilogram and 500g weights and ask how many 500g equal the kilogram. Test the answer using the balance and write it on the board.

Repeat by finding the number of 250g, 100g, 10g and 1g weights that equal a kilogram. Write the equivalents on the board as a table.

## With the lower-achievers

### With adult support

**Choose from:**

1   Prepare a collection of parcels of different weights. Tell the story that some equipment is being sent to an alien from a friendly factory owner to help him mend his broken spaceship so he can go home. The children need to weigh all the parcels to find how much they will cost to send. Working in pairs, they find the weights, which they record on a large sheet of paper. Talk about the heaviest/lightest and which will cost the most to send. The parcel postage rates give the cost for parcels within a range of weights. Choose one parcel and discuss with the children which range it comes within. So how much does it cost to send it? Repeat this with all the parcels.

2   Repeat the above activity but using scales which give the children practical experience in reading the scale to the nearest 10g or 100g.

3   Work with the children using Resource sheet 58. This gives experience in balancing to the nearest 10g. Before they begin working show the children how to start by getting something like a small pencil case nearly balanced using 100g weights and then adding 10g weights to get closer to the nearest 10g. They can count how many 100g and 10g are used and then add the two. It might help the group if they model the number using place value arrow cards.

### Teacher-independent activities

**Choose from:**

1   The children can work in pairs using a balance with some 10g and 100g weights. Ask them to find how many cubes will balance 10g and make them into a 'tower', recording the number. (Three cubes should weigh about 10g.) Continue by finding how many balance 20g, 30g and so on. When they have found how

many balance 10 x 10g, they can check using a 100g weight. The multiples can be marked on a number line later, with adult help.

2   Ask the children to collect five objects of about the same weight. Using a balance and working in pairs ask them to order the collection from lightest to heaviest using either direct comparison or by using weights.

3   Give the group a collection of familiar packaged items, such as crisps, biscuits and sweets. Ask them to find the weights on the labels, write them on pieces of card and put the weights in order.

4   Provide a collection of small items such as paper-clips, polystyrene packing, centicubes and counters. Ask the children to weigh out 10g of each different item and record in words, pictures and numbers to show the class during the plenary session. Ask them to explain why they had more of some things than others. *"Why do you think there were more bits of polystyrene than marbles?"*

## Plenary session

■   *"Can you explain how you worked out the cost of sending this big parcel?"*

■   *"This book balanced with 3 x 100g and 4 x 10g weights. Can you show this weight with your place value cards? What does it say?"*

■   Get children from the group to explain how they found the weight of a parcel and worked out the cost of postage from the chart.

■   Ask the group who completed Resource sheet 58 to tell the class how they used place value to find the weights of the things they used.

# What will it hold?

## Assessment focus

- Can the children estimate capacity and check by measuring?

## Resources

- measuring jugs and cylinders
- a collection of large and small bottles and plastic drinking cups
- coloured water and dry ingredients (rice, sugar and so on)
- cubes and dessert spoons

## With the whole class

- Put out a collection of unlabelled bottles and capacity measuring equipment. Show the class a litre jug or measuring cylinder and ask someone to choose a bottle of about that capacity. Then test to see if this is correct. Ask which of the containers has a capacity of about half a litre or 2 litres, and so on. Which of the containers has the smallest capacity? Is it more or less than half a litre? Can the children suggest which of the measuring it cylinders is best to use to measure the capacity of the small bottle and why? Draw the suggested cylinder on the board with its scale and ask a child to draw a line showing the estimated capacity of the small bottle. Test the capacity and get someone to draw the level. Compare the estimate with the actual measurement. Repeat with other bottles and use cylinders with different scales.

## With the lower-achievers

### With adult support

### Choose from:

1   Say *"Some children are going for a trip to another planet. Mum has packed some little bottles of drink."* Give each pair of children a different-sized small bottle. Show them a measuring cylinder containing 100ml of coloured water and ask them to estimate the capacity of their bottle.

*"Do you think your bottle holds more or less than 100ml? Do you think it holds twice as much? So how many millilitres is that?"* Provide a selection of measuring cylinders for the children to choose from, making sure they are able to read the scales. Ask the pairs to compare their measurement with the estimate and find how accurate they were. Discuss which bottles were the easiest to estimate and which the most difficult.

2   Using a range of bottles, the children could estimate how many of their bottles could be filled from a 1 litre and a 2 litre bottle and then do the test to find out if they were right.

3   Give each pair of children a 100ml measuring cylinder and talk about the scale up the side. Ask questions such as *"If I needed 60ml where would I fill it up to?"* and *"Where on the scale would 45ml come?"* Say that they are going to use this cylinder to mark a bottle to measure capacities up to 1 litre. Show how they can put 100ml into a litre bottle and mark the position with a pen. Ask for estimates of how many 100ml marks they will use to fill the bottle. Let the pairs continue to fill their containers, marking the scale in multiples of 100ml. Discuss how many 100ml filled the bottle, compare this with the estimate and count together in 100s up to 1000. Show a 250ml bottle and ask for estimates about how far up their measure the contents would come. Find out who was correct.

### Teacher-independent activities

### Choose from:

1   Each pair of children needs two identical pieces of card. First show them how to make a tall, thin and a short, fat open cylinder. Then say they are to estimate the number of cubes that will fill each one and write the number on the outside, then test the capacity using cubes. The cubes are counted (by grouping in 10's) and the result compared with the estimate. During the plenary session discuss some of the children's possible reasons for one of the cylinders holding more cubes than the other.

2    Give the group some different sized small bottles (between 100ml and 250ml) containing coloured water and some dessert spoons. (These hold 10ml.) Say that the bottles contain a 'magic potion' that the aliens use to disappear and they want to know how many 10ml spoonfuls each bottle holds. Tell the children to write their estimates of the capacity (in spoonfuls) on the blank label before they start and show how they can work in pairs to keep a tally of the number of 10ml in each bottle.

3    Tell the children to mark the level for 100ml of drink on a plastic cup. Then, practically they should find how many drinks of the same size could be poured from a 1 litre, 1.5 litre and 2 litre bottle. In the plenary session they can tell the others what they have discovered.

## Plenary session

■  Ask the group to explain which of the bottles' capacities were the most difficult to estimate.

■  Let the group show the measuring bottles they have made and explain the number of 100ml they measured and how they estimated the contents of the smaller bottle.

■  *"You found that 10 lots of 100ml filled a litre bottle. Can you count 10 lots of 100?"*

■  *"If 10 lots of 100ml filled a one litre bottle, how many lots of 100ml would you need for a 2 litre bottle?"*

# Number track

| 0 | 1 | 2 | 3 | 4 | 5 | 6 | 7 | 8 | 9 | 10 |

| 20 | 19 | 18 | 17 | 16 | 15 | 14 | 13 | 12 | 11 |

| 21 | 22 | 23 | 24 | 25 | 26 | 27 | 28 | 29 | 30 |

| 40 | 39 | 38 | 37 | 36 | 35 | 34 | 33 | 32 | 31 |

| 41 | 42 | 43 | 44 | 45 | 46 | 47 | 48 | 49 | 50 |

| 60 | 59 | 58 | 57 | 56 | 55 | 54 | 53 | 52 | 51 |

| 61 | 62 | 63 | 64 | 65 | 66 | 67 | 68 | 69 | 70 |

| 80 | 79 | 78 | 77 | 76 | 75 | 74 | 73 | 72 | 71 |

| 81 | 82 | 83 | 84 | 85 | 86 | 87 | 88 | 89 | 90 |

| 100 | 99 | 98 | 97 | 96 | 95 | 94 | 93 | 92 | 91 |

Notes for adults ·····························································

**Name** _____

# Number line to 30

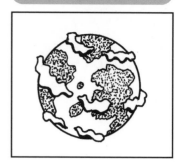

- - - - - - - - - - - - - - - - - - - - - - - - - - - - - - - - - - - - - - - - - - - - - -

```
0  1  2  3  4  5  6  7  8  9  10 11 12 13 14 15 16 17 18 19 20 21 22 23 24 25 26 27 28 29 30
```

- - - - - - - - - - - - - - - - - - - - - - - - - - - - - - - - - - - - - - - - - - - - - -

- - - - - - - - - - - - - - - - - - - - - - - - - - - - - - - - - - - - - - - - - - - - - -

- - - - - - - - - - - - - - - - - - - - - - - - - - - - - - - - - - - - - - - - - - - - - -

**Notes for adults** • • • • • • • • • • • • • • • • • • • • • • • • • • • • • • • • • •

You can cut along the lines and stick the strips together to make a line beyond 30.

**Name** _____

# Number line to 50

- - - - - - - - - - - - - - - - - - - - - - - - - - - - - - - - - - - - - - - - - - -

```
├───┼───┼───┼───┼───┼───┼───┼───┼───┼───┤
0      10      20      30      40      50
```

- - - - - - - - - - - - - - - - - - - - - - - - - - - - - - - - - - - - - - - - - - -

```
├───┼───┼───┼───┼───┼───┼───┼───┼───┼───┤
```

- - - - - - - - - - - - - - - - - - - - - - - - - - - - - - - - - - - - - - - - - - -

```
├───┼───┼───┼───┼───┼───┼───┼───┼───┼───┤
```

- - - - - - - - - - - - - - - - - - - - - - - - - - - - - - - - - - - - - - - - - - -

**Notes for adults** • • • • • • • • • • • • • • • • • • • • • • • • • • • • • • • • • • •

You can cut along the lines and stick the strips together to make a line beyond 50.

# 100 square

| 1 | 2 | 3 | 4 | 5 | 6 | 7 | 8 | 9 | 10 |
|---|---|---|---|---|---|---|---|---|---|
| 11 | 12 | 13 | 14 | 15 | 16 | 17 | 18 | 19 | 20 |
| 21 | 22 | 23 | 24 | 25 | 26 | 27 | 28 | 29 | 30 |
| 31 | 32 | 33 | 34 | 35 | 36 | 37 | 38 | 39 | 40 |
| 41 | 42 | 43 | 44 | 45 | 46 | 47 | 48 | 49 | 50 |
| 51 | 52 | 53 | 54 | 55 | 56 | 57 | 58 | 59 | 60 |
| 61 | 62 | 63 | 64 | 65 | 66 | 67 | 68 | 69 | 70 |
| 71 | 72 | 73 | 74 | 75 | 76 | 77 | 78 | 79 | 80 |
| 81 | 82 | 83 | 84 | 85 | 86 | 87 | 88 | 89 | 90 |
| 91 | 92 | 93 | 94 | 95 | 96 | 97 | 98 | 99 | 100 |

Notes for adults • • • • • • • • • • • • • • • • • • • • • • • • • • • • • • • • •

• • • • • • • • • • • • • • • • • • • • • • •

# Empty 100 square

# Where does it go?

Write where the numbers go on the lines.

**1.**

0       5       10

7

**2.**

0       5       10

2

**3.**

5       10       15

12

**4.**

10       15       20

13

Write the missing numbers.

**5.**

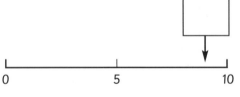

**6.**

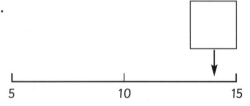

**7.**

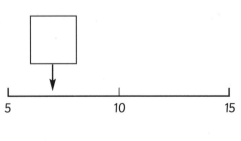

**8.**

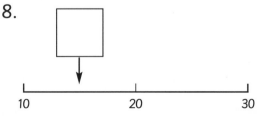

# Number line counting

1.

☐                    ☐

2.

☐                    ☐

3.

☐                    ☐

4.

☐                    ☐

5.

☐                    ☐

# Counting on and back

0  1  2  3  4  5  6  7  8  9

16  15  14  13  12  11  10

17

18  19  20  21  22  23  24  25  26

30  29  28  27

1. Start on ☐   Count on ☐   I land on ☐

2. Start on ☐   Count on ☐   I land on ☐

3. Start on ☐   Count back ☐   I land on ☐

4. Start on ☐   Count back ☐   I land on ☐

5. Count from ☐ to ☐

How many did you count? ☐

# Missing numbers

Write the missing numbers.

1.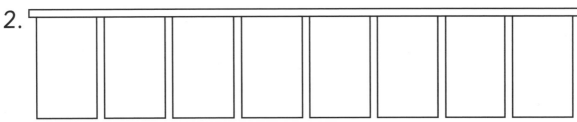

2.

3.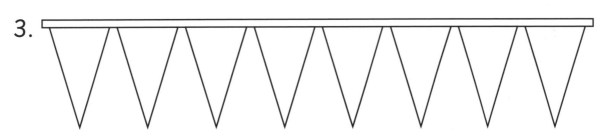

4.

Write some numbers of your own.

5.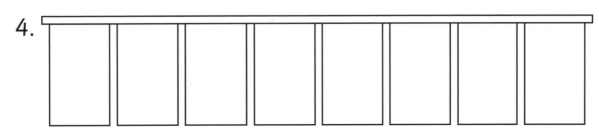

# What's the order?

Use a number line to help put the numbers in order.

1.

| 9 | 19 | 5 | 14 |
|---|----|---|----|
|   |    |   |    |

smallest                               largest

2.

| 10 | 21 | 6 | 38 |
|----|----|---|----|
|    |    |   |    |

largest                             smallest

3.

| 50 | 25 | 16 | 31 |
|----|----|----|----|
|    |    |    |    |

smallest                           largest

|   |   |   |   |
|---|---|---|---|
|   |   |   |   |

largest                             smallest

4. Make 4 more two-digit numbers with your arrow cards.
   Put them in order.

Notes for adults • • • • • • • • • • • • • • • • • • • • • • • • • • • • • • •

# Getting bigger and bigger

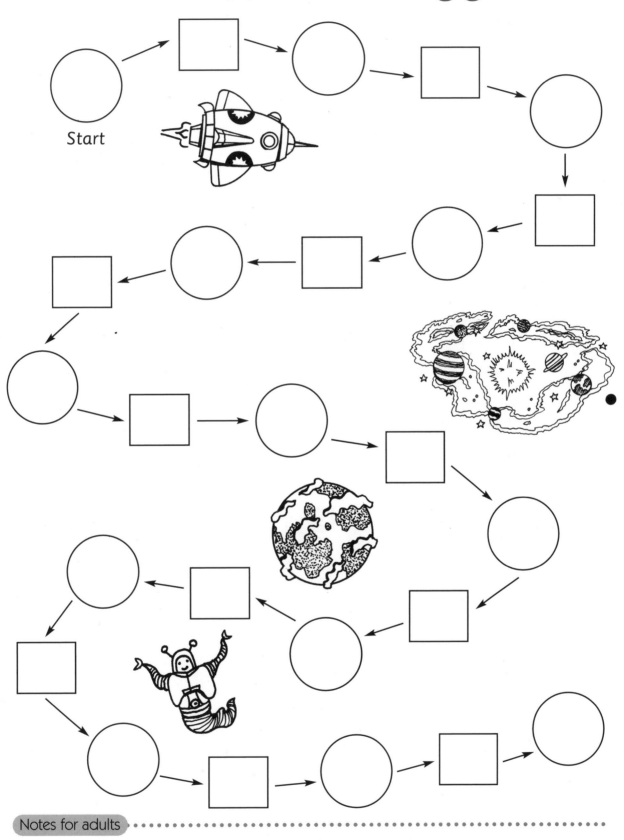

# Fill them in

1.
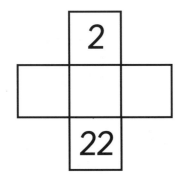

2.
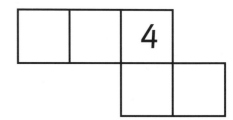

3.
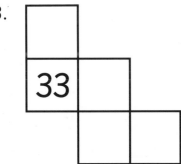

4.
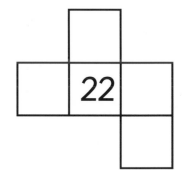

5.
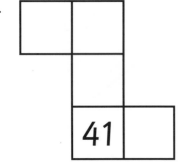

6.
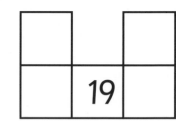

7.
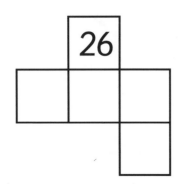

8.
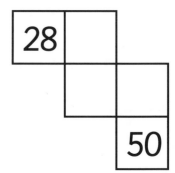

# Hexagon game

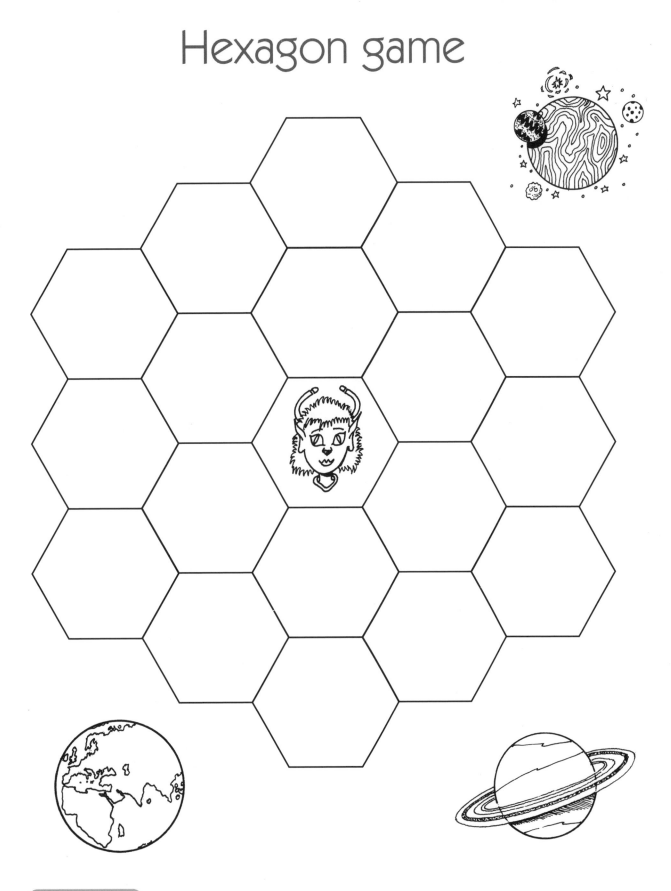

# Space dogs – make 10's

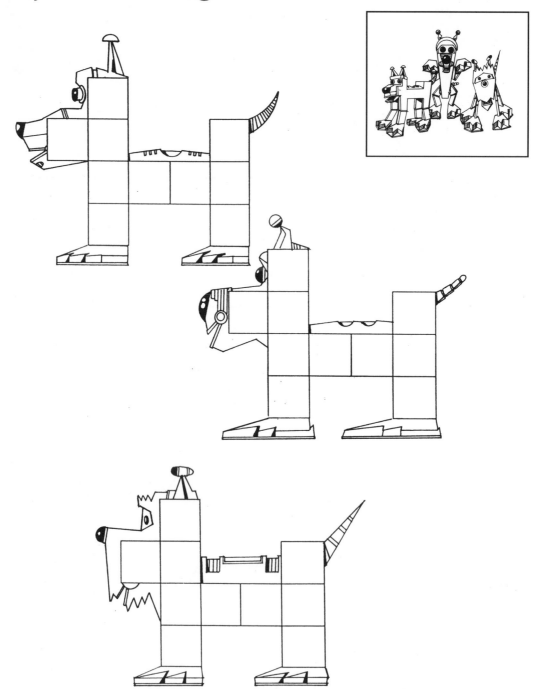

I have made ⬜ whole dogs and ⬜ parts.

I used ⬜ cubes.

# Making arrays with stamps

# More than and less than

 Make the first number more.

1. [ ] [ ] > [ ] [ ]

2. [ ] [ ] > [ ] [ ]

3. [ ] [ ] > [ ] [ ]

4. [ ] [ ] > [ ] [ ]

 Now make the first number less.

5. [ ] [ ] < [ ] [ ]

6. [ ] [ ] < [ ] [ ]

7. [ ] [ ] < [ ] [ ]

Notes for adults •••••••••••••••••••••••••••••••••••••••••••

# The even number muncher

- Find odd and even numbers.
- Write even numbers in the robot's tummy.
- Put odd numbers in the bin.

Yum! I love to eat even numbers.

- Take a handful of cubes.
- Count them and then try to make pairs.
- If you can make a pair write that even number in the robot's tummy.
- If you cannot make a pair write that odd number in the bin.

**Name** _____

# Adding odds
# and evens

You need:

Throw the two dice and write the numbers
in the boxes. Then add the two numbers.

My numbers are:                              The answer is:

1.  ▢▢   ◯ + ◯ = ◯        odd        even

2.  ▢▢   ◯ + ◯ = ◯        odd        even

3.  ▢▢   ◯ + ◯ = ◯        odd        even

4.  ▢▢   ◯ + ◯ = ◯        odd        even

5.  ▢▢   ◯ + ◯ = ◯        odd        even

Now try adding 3 numbers.

# Spot the odds and evens

1. Start at 0. Hop in 2's to the end of the line.

0  1  2  3  4  5  6  7  8  9  10  11  12  13  14  15  16  17  18  19  20  21  22  23  24  25

2. Did you hop on the odd or even numbers?

3. Write the missing numbers in the triangle.
   - Colour the even numbers red.
   - Colour the odd numbers blue.

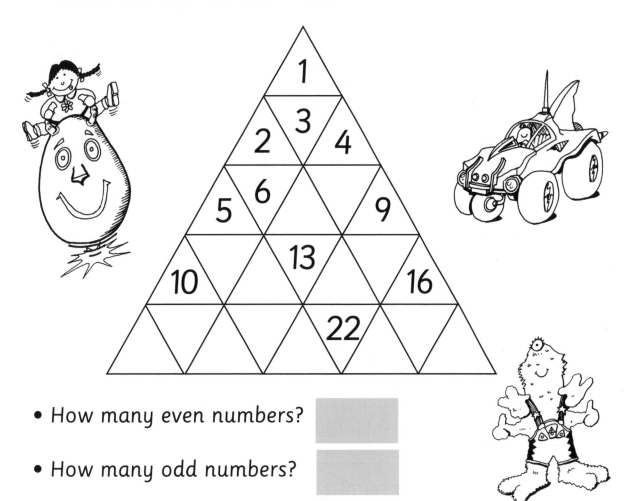

- How many even numbers?

- How many odd numbers?

# What's missing?

Use a number line to help you.

Circles: 1, 3, 5, _, 9, _, 13, _, _

1. To make the pattern I counted in ▢

Circles: 18, _, _, 12, 10, _, 6, 4

2. To make the pattern I counted in ▢

Circles: 14, _, 16, 17, _, 19, _, 21, _

3. To make the pattern I counted in ▢

4. Now you choose a number pattern.

Notes for adults • • • • • • • • • • • • • • • • • • • • • • • • • • • • • • • • • • • •

• • • • • • • • • • • • • • • • • • • • • • • •

76

# The magic machine

1.

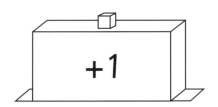

| In | | Out |
|----|----|-----|
| 1 | ⟶ | 2 |
| 2 | ⟶ | 3 |
| 3 | ⟶ | |
| 4 | ⟶ | |
| 5 | ⟶ | |

2.

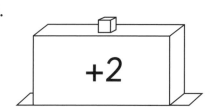

| In | | Out |
|----|----|-----|
| 1 | ⟶ | 3 |
| 2 | ⟶ | 4 |
| 3 | ⟶ | |
| 4 | ⟶ | |
| 5 | ⟶ | |

3.

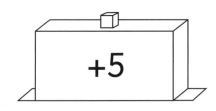

| In | | Out |
|----|----|-----|
| 1 | ⟶ | 6 |
| 2 | ⟶ | |
| 3 | ⟶ | |
| 4 | ⟶ | |
| 5 | ⟶ | |

4. Choose your own number.

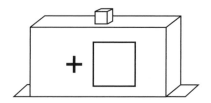

| In | | Out |
|----|----|-----|
| 1 | ⟶ | |
| 2 | ⟶ | |
| 3 | ⟶ | |
| 4 | ⟶ | |
| 5 | ⟶ | |

# Aim for 10

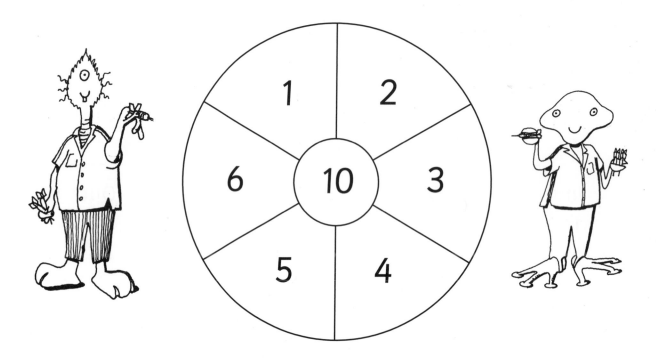

Find ways to make 10

1. 1 + 3 + ☐ = 10    2. 4 + ☐ + 5 = 10

3. 6 + *3* + *1* = 10    4. 2 + *5* + *3* = 10

5. *5* + *4* + *1* = 10    6. *6* + *3* + *1* = 10

7. *5* + *3* + *2* = 10    8. ☐ + ☐ + ☐ = 10

9. ☐ + ☐ + ☐ = 10    10. ☐ ☐ ☐ ☐ 10

Make 10 with 4 numbers.

# Aim for ☐

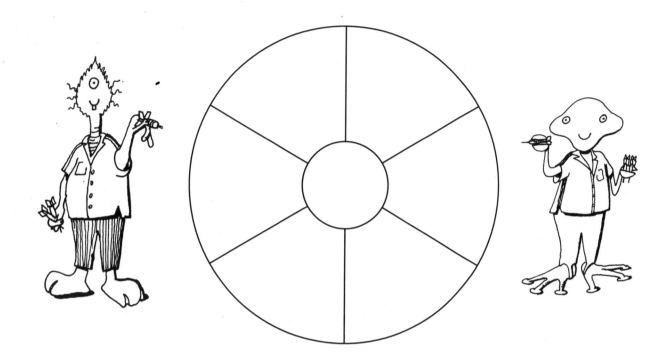

Find ways to make ▭

1. ▢ + ▢ + ▢ = ▢       2. ▢ + ▢ + ▢ = ▢

3. ▢ + ▢ + ▢ = ▢       4. ▢ + ▢ + ▢ = ▢

5. ▢ + ▢ + ▢ = ▢       6. ▢ + ▢ + ▢ = ▢

7. ▢ + ▢ + ▢ = ▢       8. ▢ + ▢ + ▢ = ▢

9. ▢ + ▢ + ▢ = ▢      10. ▢ + ▢ + ▢ = ▢

Notes for adults · · · · · · · · · · · · · · · · · · · · · · · · · · · · · · · · · ·

· · · · · · · · · · · · · · · · · · · · · · · · · ·

# Pick 3 numbers

Add 3 numbers to make the number on the label.
Write the numbers on the balloons.

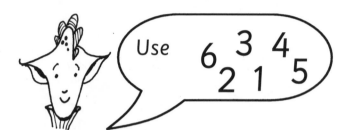

Use 6 2 3 4 1 5

1.
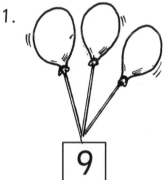

9

2.

10

3.

12

4.
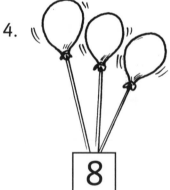

8

5.
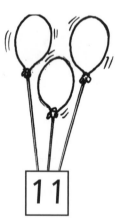

11

6.
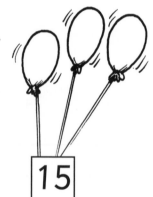

15

Choose 3 more numbers. Make a sum with them.

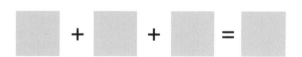

☐ + ☐ + ☐ = ☐

Notes for adults • • • • • • • • • • • • • • • • • • • • • • • • • • • • • • • • • • •

# Dotty dominoes – 1

1.

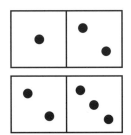

$1 + 2 + 2 + 3 =$ 

2.

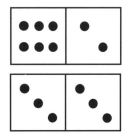

$6 + 2 + 3 + 3 =$ 

3.

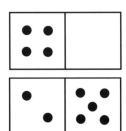

 $+$  $+$  $+$  $=$ 

4.

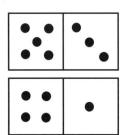

 $+$  $+$  $+$  $=$ 

5.

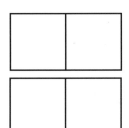

 $+$  $+$  $+$  $=$ 

6.

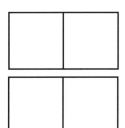

 $+$  $+$  $+$  $=$ 

Notes for adults

# Dotty dominoes – 2

1.

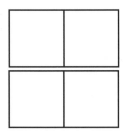

 +  +  +  =

2.

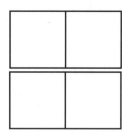

 +  +  +  =

3.

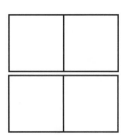

 +  +  +  =

4.

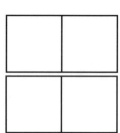

 +  +  +  =

5.

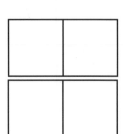

 +  +  +  =

6.

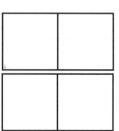

 +  +  +  =

Notes for adults •••••••••••••••••••••••••••••••••••••••••••

•••••••••••••••••••••••••••

# 10 spotting

Add the numbers on the cards by spotting the 10's.

1. $2$ + $6$ + $4$

$2 + 10 = \square$

2. $2$ + $6$ + $8$

$\square + \square = \square$

3. $7$ + $5$ + $5$

4. $7$ + $7$ + $3$

5. $9$ + $1$ + $1$

6. $5$ + $2$ + $3$

Notes for adults • • • • • • • • • • • • • • • • • • • • • • • • • • • • • • • • • •

# Shopping

1p   2p   3p   4p   5p   6p

Buy ☐ things.

7p   8p   9p

1. I bought

Cost ☐ p

2. I bought

Cost ☐ p

3. I bought

Cost ☐ p

4. I bought

Cost ☐ p

5. I bought

Cost ☐ p

Notes for adults ● ● ● ● ● ● ● ● ● ● ● ● ● ● ● ● ● ● ● ● ● ● ● ● ● ● ● ● ● ● ● ● ● ●

# The adding game

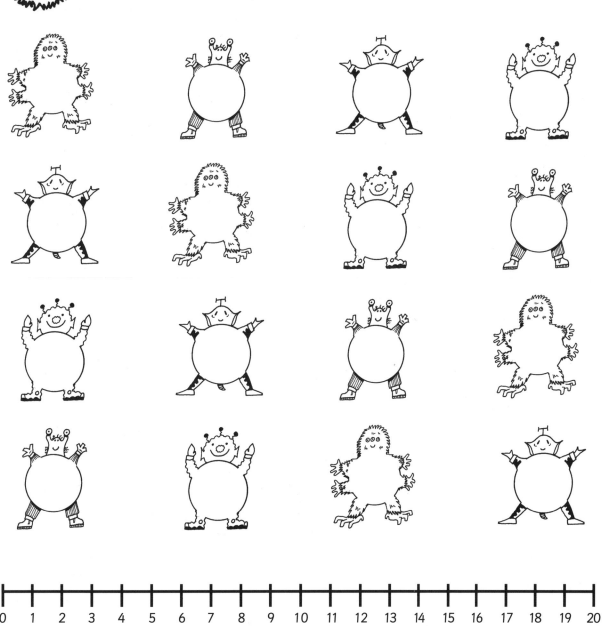

The first person to cross out all the numbers on their aliens WINS!

0  1  2  3  4  5  6  7  8  9  10  11  12  13  14  15  16  17  18  19  20

# What's the score?

Circle numbers to make the score.

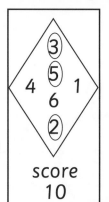

3
5
4 1
6
2
score
10

1.

3
5
4 1
6
2

Score

2.

3
5
4 1
6
2

Score

3.

3
5
4 1
6
2

Score

4.

3
5
4 1
6
2

Score

5.

3
5
4 1
6
2

Score

6.

3
5
4 1
6
2

Score

Notes for adults ● ● ● ● ● ● ● ● ● ● ● ● ● ● ● ● ● ● ● ● ● ● ● ● ● ● ● ● ● ● ● ● ● ● ● ● ● ● ● ● ● ● ●

# Race game

# Space creatures

Join the aliens who make 10.

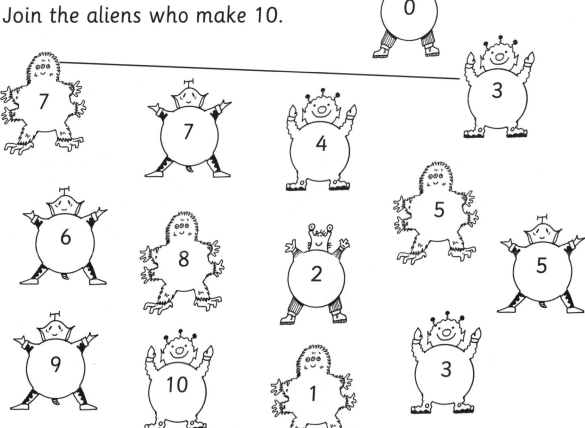

Write your pairs in order.

$0 + 10 =$ `10`          $4 + $ ☐ $= $ ☐          $8 + $ ☐ $= $ ☐

$1 + 9 = $ ☐          $5 + $ ☐ $= $ ☐          $9 + $ ☐ $= $ ☐

$2 + $ ☐ $= $ ☐          $6 + $ ☐ $= $ ☐          $10 + $ ☐ $= $ ☐

$3 + $ ☐ $= $ ☐          $7 + $ ☐ $= $ ☐

Notes for adults

# Making patterns

1.

2.

3. Now you make some number patterns.

# Three in a row

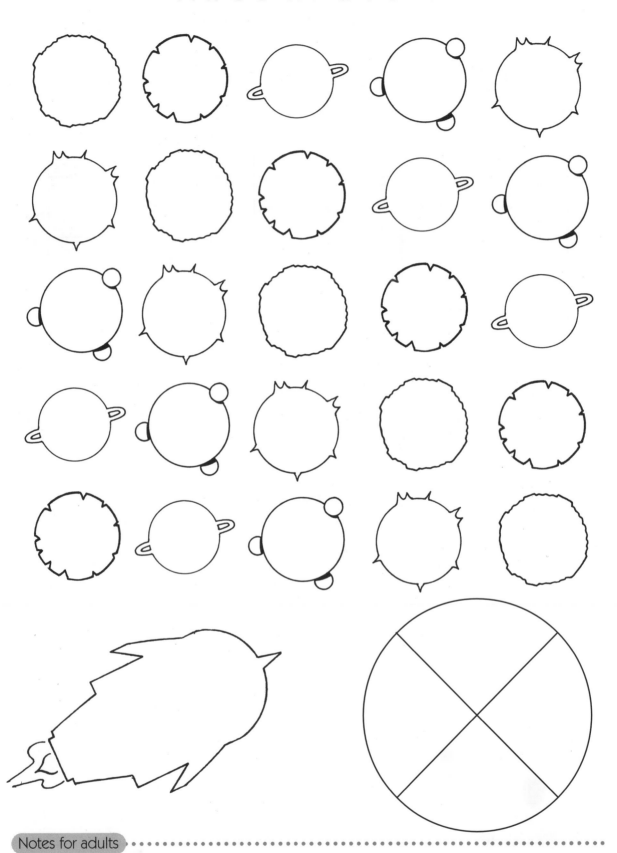

# Loop cards

+5

12

−7

17

+6

10

−9

16

+8

7

+5

15

−6

20

−8

14

+6

6

# Blank loop cards

# Making stories

1.

3 aliens come out of the ship.
2 more come.

2.

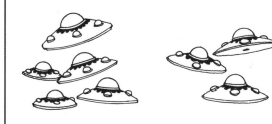

8 space ships. 3 fly away.

Now tell these stories.

3.

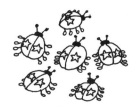

4.

Make up some stories.

**Notes for adults** • • • • • • • • • • • • • • • • • • • • • • • • • • • • • • • • • • • • • • •

Focus onto key words that indicate either addition or subtraction.

# Round and round

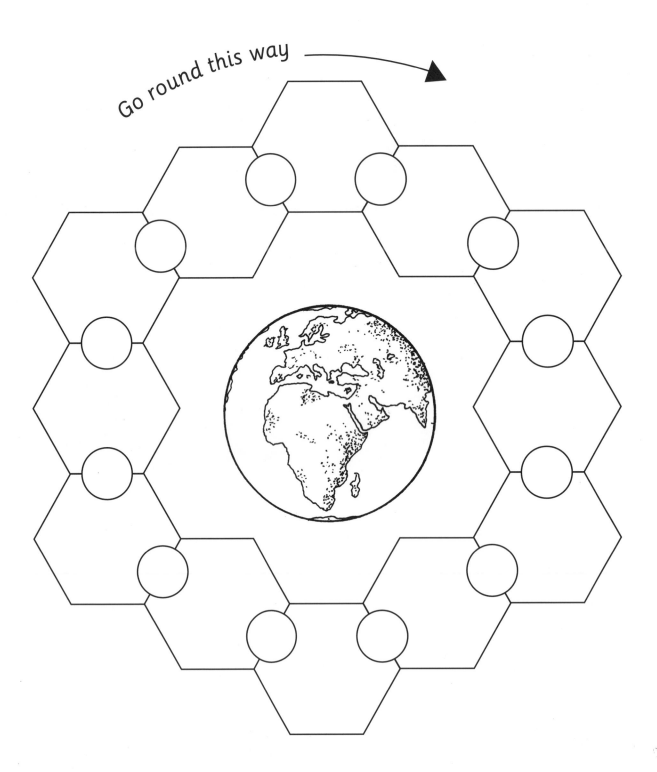

Go round this way

# Going nowhere

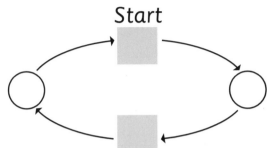

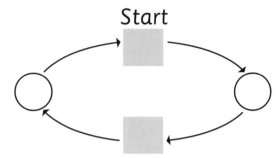

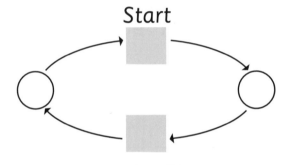

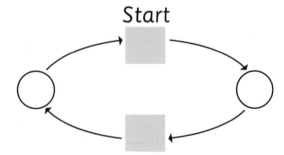

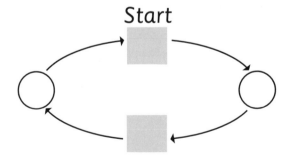

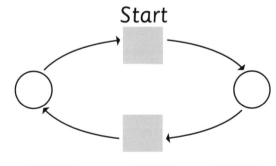

# Take 3 numbers

Use the 3 numbers to write the number sentences.

1.

2
8
10

2 + 8 = 10

8 + 2 = ☐

10 − 2 = ☐

10 − 8 = ☐

2.
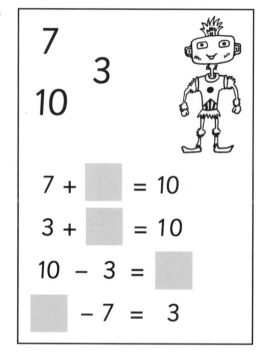

7
3
10

7 + ☐ = 10

3 + ☐ = 10

10 − 3 = ☐

☐ − 7 = 3

3.

6   10
4

☐ + ☐ = ☐

☐ + ☐ = ☐

☐ − ☐ = ☐

☐ − ☐ = ☐

4.

15
7   8

# Adding 10's and 1's

```
  ( )  →+1→  ( )  →+1→  ( )  →+1→  ( )
   ↓+10       ↓+10       ↓+10       ↓+10
  ( )  →+1→  ( )  →+1→  ( )  →+1→  ( )
   ↓+10       ↓+10       ↓+10       ↓+10
  ( )  →+1→  ( )  →+1→  ( )  →+1→  ( )
   ↓+10       ↓+10       ↓+10       ↓+10
  ( )  →+1→  ( )  →+1→  ( )  →+1→  ( )
```

What happens to the units when 1 is added?

What happens to the units when 10 is added?

# Aliens game – 1

| | | |
|---|---|---|
| 20 <br> 85 | 80   35 <br> 30 | 65 <br> 50 |
| 15 <br> 90 <br> 25 | 70 <br> 10   25 <br> 40 | 50 <br> 75 <br> 10 |
| 75 <br> 55 <br> 5 | 60 <br> 45   60 <br> 65 | 90 <br> 40 <br> 50 |
| 95 <br> 85 | 35 <br> 15   70 | 50 <br> 30 |

# Aliens game – 2

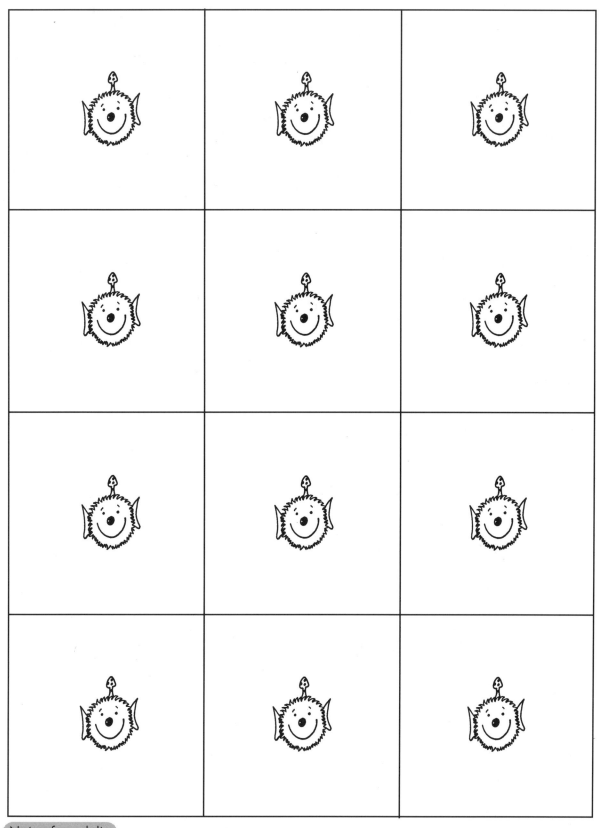

Notes for adults

# On from the 10's

1.  10 + 12 splits into

    10 + 10 + 2 = [ ]          so   10 + 12 = [ ]

    +10        +2

    10        20

2.  20 + 14 splits into

    20 + 10 + 4 = [ ]          so   20 + 14 = [ ]

3.  30 + 19 splits into

    30 + 10 + 9 = [ ]          so   30 + 19 = [ ]

4.  20 + 26 splits into

    20 + 10 + 10 + 6 = [ ]          so   20 + 26 = [ ]

Now try these:     40 + 11          30 + 25          20 + 28

Notes for adults • • • • • • • • • • • • • • • • • • • • • • • • • • • • • • • • • • • • • • • • •

**Name** _____

# Crossing the 10's

Show your number line jumps.

| | |
|---|---|
| 1.  = □ <br><br> _____ | 2. □ ○ □ = □ <br><br> _____ |
| 3.  ○ □ = □ <br><br> _____ | 4.   =  <br><br> _____ |
| 5.  ○  = □ <br><br> _____ | 6.  □ =  <br><br> _____ |
| 7.  ○  = □ <br><br> _____ | 8.  □ =  <br><br> _____ |

Notes for adults ••••••••••••••••••••••••• Resource sheet 45 ••••••

••••••••••••••••••••••••••••••••••••••••

# Planets game

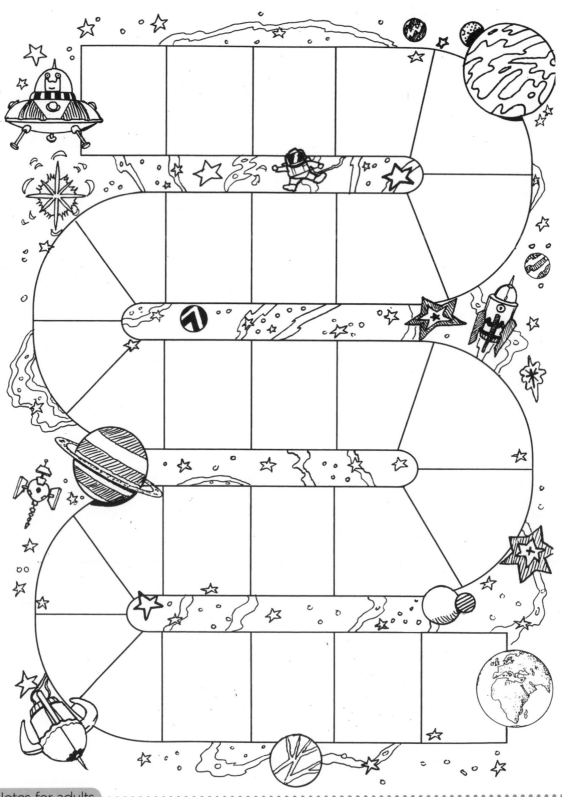

# Buying for 2

9p

15p

12p

10p

20p

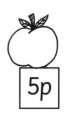
5p

Buy 2.

1.     $9p + 9p = \boxed{\phantom{00}}\ p$    $2 \times 9 = \boxed{\phantom{00}}\ p$

2.     $5p + 5p = \boxed{\phantom{00}}\ p$    $2 \times 5 = \boxed{\phantom{00}}\ p$

3.     $12p + \boxed{\phantom{00}}\ p = \boxed{\phantom{00}}\ p$    $2 \times \boxed{\phantom{00}} = \boxed{\phantom{00}}\ p$

4.     $\boxed{\phantom{00}}\ p + \boxed{\phantom{00}}\ p = \boxed{\phantom{00}}\ p$    $2 \times \boxed{\phantom{00}} = \boxed{\phantom{00}}\ p$

5.     $\boxed{\phantom{00}}\ p + \boxed{\phantom{00}}\ p = \boxed{\phantom{00}}\ p$    $2 \times \boxed{\phantom{00}} = \boxed{\phantom{00}}\ p$

6.     $\boxed{\phantom{00}}\ p + \boxed{\phantom{00}}\ p = \boxed{\phantom{00}}\ p$    $2 \times \boxed{\phantom{00}} = \boxed{\phantom{00}}\ p$

Notes for adults ●●●●●●●●●●●●●●●●●●●●●●●●●●●●●●●●●●●●●●●

# Sale in space

Everything in the space centre shop is now HALF PRICE.
Find the missing prices.

| toy space cat | |
|---|---|
| Old price | 50p |
| New price | 25p |

| space helmet | |
|---|---|
| Old price | 28p |
| New price | p |

| star lolly | |
|---|---|
| Old price | 16p |
| New price | p |

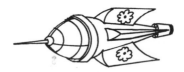

| toy rocket | |
|---|---|
| Old price | 24p |
| New price | p |

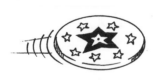

| space wizzer | |
|---|---|
| Old price | 42p |
| New price | p |

| space comic | |
|---|---|
| Old price | p |
| New price | 15p |

Notes for adults • • • • • • • • • • • • • • • • • • • • • • • •

# Doubling and halving

You need 1–10 cards. Turn over one card and write the number in the box.

Put the number into the machines.

double    half

start number

1. 

2. 

3. 

4. 

5. 

6. 

What happens to the numbers?

Notes for adults ••••••••••••••••••••••••••••••••••••••••

# Fractions

Design a flag for another planet.
Colour half of each flag in red and
half in green. Each flag must be different.

1.
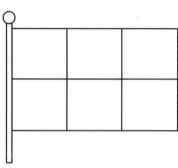

2.
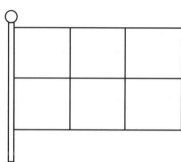

3.
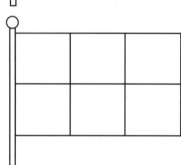

4.
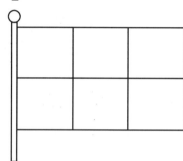

5. How many squares are coloured on each flag?

Half of 6 is

Colour half of each flag in a different way.

6.
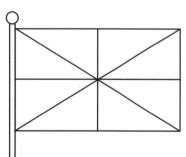

7.
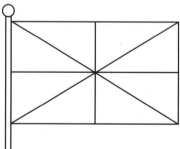

8. How many triangles are coloured on each flag?

Half of 8 is

# Finding fractions

I am working with  cubes.

I can find $\frac{1}{2}$.    Yes     No

$\frac{1}{2}$ of  is

---

I can find $\frac{1}{4}$.    Yes     No

$\frac{1}{4}$ of  is

---

I can find $\frac{1}{3}$.    Yes     No

$\frac{1}{3}$ of  is

---

I can find $\frac{1}{5}$.    Yes     No

$\frac{1}{5}$ of  is

---

I can find $\frac{1}{10}$.    Yes     No

$\frac{1}{10}$ of  is

---

Notes for adults • • • • • • • • • • • • • • • • • • • • • • Resource sheet 51 • • •

• • • • • • • • • • • • • • • • • • • • • • • • • •

# Aliens fractions game

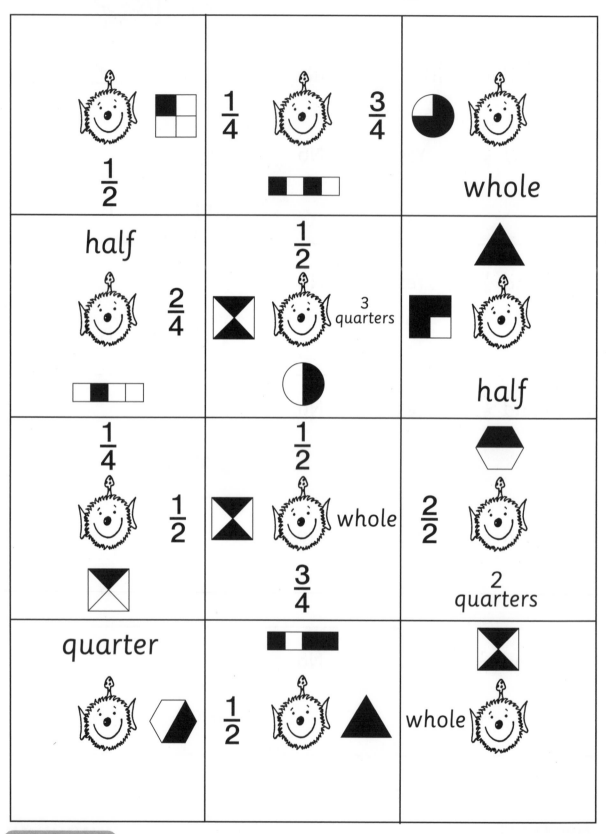

# Balancing 50 grams

You need the equipment shown below.

Put the 50g in one pan and find out how many of each thing will balance it. Write the number in the circle.

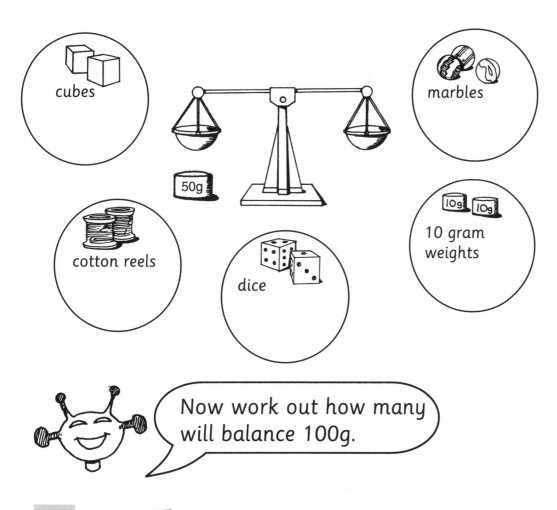

Now work out how many will balance 100g.

cubes  will balance 100g.

marbles  will balance 100g.

cotton reels  will balance 100g.

dice  will balance 100g.

10g weights  will balance 100g.

# Space snacks

Space candy

12p

Star drink

10p

Mars apple

6p

Moon cake

15p

Solar ice cream

20p

1. Zendo buys a drink  and candy  . She pays  [    ] p

   Tanit buys an apple  and a cake  . He pays  [    ] p

   Who spends most? [              ]

2. Joz has 40p.  How many drinks  can she buy? [        ]

3. Ruvik spent 60p on ice cream. How many did he buy? [        ]

4.  3 aliens buy an apple each.

   They spend [    p]

On the back of this sheet, write a story about a snack you would buy at the space station.

# Working it out

1. Joz has 2 moon cakes.   Zendo has 6 moon cakes.

   How many altogether?

   Write a number sentence:  +  =

   Who has the most moon cakes?

2.

   Cinema starts              Cinema ends

   What time does the Cinema start?

   When does it end?

   How long is the film?

3.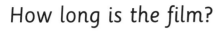

   4 aliens have a bag of 16 Mars apples to share equally.

   How many each?

4. Write a story using the numbers 10 and 5.

# How much money?

Draw the coins in the money chests

1. 40p
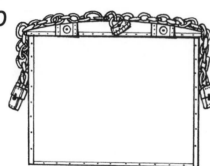

2. 33p
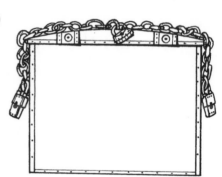

3. 29p
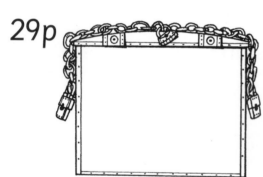

4. 56p
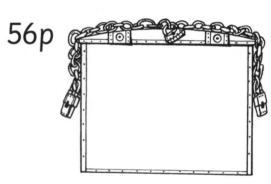

How much money is there?

5.
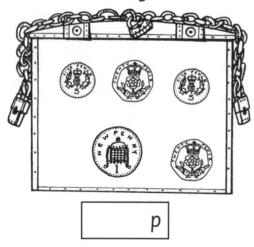

| | p |
|---|---|

6.
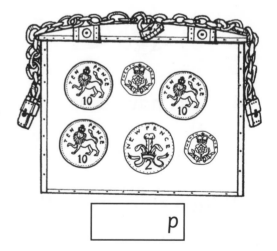

| | p |
|---|---|

# Space shopping

Space wizzer

50p

Moon bird

£4

Space pet

£5

Solar ice cream

50p

Star drum

£2

Asteroid game

£6

1. How much are a Moon bird and a Star drum?

2. How much are two space pets?

3. What 2 items cost £10?

4. What 3 items cost £12?

5. Buy an ice cream. How much change from £1?

6. Buy 2 wizzers. How much change from £5?

7. Find ways to spend £10.

Notes for adults · · · · · · · · · · · · · · · · · · · · · · · · · · · · · · · · · · · · · · · · · · · ·

# How heavy?

You need:

book          apple

balance          weights          shoe          cup

1. A book  is ▯ 100g and ▯ 10g.

   It weighs ▯ g.

2. An apple  is ▯ 100g and ▯ 10g.

   It weighs ▯ g.

3. A shoe  is ▯ 100g and ▯ 10g.

   It weighs ▯ g.

4. A cup  is ▯ 100g and ▯ 10g.

   It weighs ▯ g.

5. The _____ is heaviest.

   The _____ is lightest.

6. Weigh 3 more things using 100g and 10g.

Notes for adults • • • • • • • • • • • • • • • • • • • • • • • • • • • • • • • •

# Clip art

 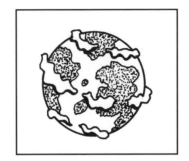 

 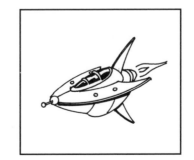 

# Money clip art

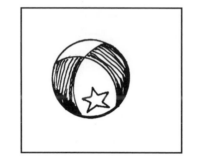

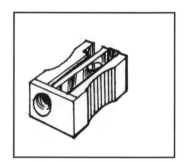

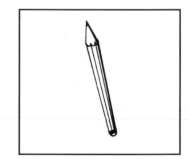

# List of Assessment Focuses

| Assessment focus | Chapter | Date achieved / comments |
|---|---|---|
| Can the children estimate the number of objects in a collection and count by grouping? | 1 | |
| Can the children estimate where numbers go on a number line? | 1 | |
| Can the children put sets of numbers in order? | 2 | |
| Can the children use a number line or 100 square to count on and back in 1s, 10s, and 100s? | 2 | |
| Can the children group into 10s and 1s for counting and use partitioning? | 2 | |
| Can the children compare and order numbers using a range of vocabulary, eg larger/smaller and more than/less than, and begin to use the symbols? | 2 | |
| Can the children recognise and use odd and even numbers? | 3 | |
| Can the children recognise two-digit multiples of 2, 5 and 10? | 3 | |
| Can the children complete a given number sequences and describe the rule? | 3 | |
| Can the children add three or more numbers and explain how they worked? | 4 | |
| Can the children add numbers by finding pairs that make 10? | 4 | |
| Can the children recognise and use patterns in addition, particularly to make the number bonds of 10 and 20? | 4 | |
| Can the children make decisions about addition and subtraction? | 5 | |
| Can the children use corresponding addition and subtraction facts? | 5 | |
| Can the children add or subtract multiples of 1 or 10 from a given number? | 5 | |
| Can the children use a number line for addition and subtraction? | 6 | |
| Can the children add or subtract crossing the 10's boundary? | 6 | |
| Can the children find the difference between a pair of numbers by counting on or back? | 6 | |

| Assessment focus | Chapter | Date achieved / comments |
|---|---|---|
| Can the children understand that doubling is the same as multiplying by 2 and halving is the same as dividing by 2? | 7 | |
| Can the children use and describe multiplication arrays? | 7 | |
| Can the children use a repeated addition or subtraction for multiplication and division? | 7 | |
| Can the children find fractions of shapes and numbers and explain their work? | 8 | |
| Can the children position fractions on a number line? | 8 | |
| Can the children use simple fractions in a practical situation? | 8 | |
| Can the children explain their solutions to a variety of problems? | 9 | |
| Can the children solve problems and write number stories to reflect practical situations? | 9 | |
| Can the children solve problems using money? | 9 | |
| Can the children suggest appropriate units for measuring length and work with increasing accuracy? | 10 | |
| Can the children use a balance to compare and order weights? | 10 | |
| Can the children estimate capacity and check by measuring? | 10 | |